THE MODERN CARPENTER AND JOINER

VOLUME III

Fig. 1.—MODERN HALF-TIMBERING—TUDOR HOUSE, ARGYLL PLACE.
By Edwin T. Hall, F.R.I.B.A., F.R.San.I., and E. Stanley Hall, M.A., F.R.I.B.A.

THE
MODERN CARPENTER
AND JOINER

BY
HARRY BRYANT NEWBOLD, F.R.I.B.A.
PAST MEMBER OF THE COUNCIL OF THE SOCIETY OF ARCHITECTS
LATE EDITOR OF "THE NATIONAL BUILDER"
AUTHOR OF "MODERN PRACTICAL BUILDING"

WITH
SPECIAL SECTIONS ON
THE USE OF THE STEEL SQUARE
BY
HAROLD RYDER

VOLUME III

THE CAXTON PUBLISHING COMPANY, LIMITED
CLUN HOUSE, SURREY STREET, LONDON, W.C.2.

*Made and Printed in Great Britain by
Hazell, Watson & Viney, Ltd., London and Aylesbury.*
2639

CONTENTS

VOL. III

CHAPTER I

TURRETS AND BAY-WINDOWS

CHAPTER II

FRAME CONSTRUCTION

CHAPTER III

JOINERY: INTRODUCTORY AND WINDOWS

CHAPTER IV

JOINERY: DOORS AND WOOD FINISHINGS TO ROOMS

CHAPTER V

FITTINGS

CONTENTS

CHAPTER VI

VERANDAHS, BALCONIES AND GARDEN FURNITURE

CHAPTER VII

WOOD CARVING

INDEX

FULL-PAGE PLATES

VOL. III

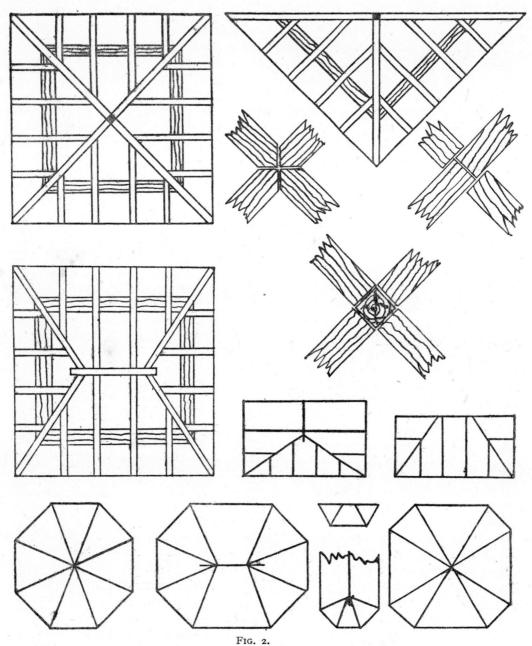

FIG. 2.

Upper line.—(1) A square turret of even pitch. (2) Half the turret used to roof an angle bay. (3) Methods of treating meeting-point of the hips.

Second line.—(1) The same square turret roofed with uneven pitches. (2 and 3) Half of this turret employed to cover a square bay. (2) With sharper pitch to the front. (3) With two sharper pitches upon the wings.

Third line.—(1) The regular octagon roof. (2) The octagon with a section of straight roofing inserted. (3) The hexagonal bay. (4) The octagonal bay. (5) The irregular octagon.

2

SQUARE TURRETS AND ANGLE-BAYS

Where the main building is planned upon a square or oblong, or upon any combination of these two figures, the main block is usually one complete unit. Smaller additions are frequently only slices taken from the larger figure, but the method that will roof the whole is available for roofing any lesser part. Fig. 2 shows a small ventilator turret, square on plan and measuring 4' 9" over its plates. The elevation indicates that this turret is also of the 15" pitch. With plates of equal length and a roof of even pitch, plainly there can be no ridge and all hips will pitch together at their points.

Fig. 2 shows several alternative fashions in which the heads of these hips may be treated, according to the requirements of the case and the convenience of the roofer. First we may set out and cut a pair of these hips to pitch together like a pair of rafters set across the diagonal of this building. But the opposite pair that will cross them at right angles must then each be cut back by one-half of the hip thickness, to allow the first pair to pass between them. We have now two different lengths of hips in this one small roof. If cut in advance and the fact forgotten, considerable trouble may be caused by pitching the roof upon hips of wrong length. To avoid this, and make our after-operations fool-proof, we may cut all four hips to the one pattern. It is shown next how this may be done with four equal hips, splayed both to right and to left. These four hip points are now pitched together at one time, and give a perfect intersection. These double splays can be avoided and all hips cut square through, if a square finial block is employed to bring all four hips to the same length, as is shown in the following illustration.

This turret measures 4' 9" across its plates. Where no finial is used, the span of a single rafter to its centre is then 2' 4½". Setting the square to our foot-span pitch figures, we step up 2' of span and measure on from this last mark with square or rule for the odd 4½" in the span. With 2' 4½" of span stepped off, we have our finished rafter length from which we can set out the jacks. Setting next to 17 and 15, we step out 2' of span upon the hips, and have now to measure forward from this mark, not by 4½", but by the diagonal of a square of which 4½" forms the side. By measurement upon the square we find this diagonal to be about 6⅜", and with rule or the square we add this horizontal measurement to the span already given to the hip pattern.

PARTS AND WHOLES

Steel-square learners who could roof a square shed with confidence have been extremely puzzled to produce the lengths and cuts for an angle-bay, such as is shown in Fig. 2. Yet comparing this roof with that of the square shed, it is seen to be only a half-slice upon the diagonal line. The wall hips shown in its elevation stand at exactly the same inclination as those of the main roof above, and show that the rafter also is of the main 15″ pitch. If in error the pitch of these wall hips should be taken as the pitch of this roof, the whole will be considerably flatter than intended by the architect. Since these wall lines actually denote hips, whatever rise they make in the 17″ of hip run will also be made by the rafter pattern in its foot of span. Entirely to his own convenience, the roofer may choose to set out upon face or wall side of these hips. Span of the two hips marked upon the wall face is equal to width across the angle-bay, in this case 6′ 8¾″. If we wish to place the setting-out marks upon the outer face of these hips, then the span is reduced by thickness of two 2″ hips to 6′ 4¾″. Half of this span, or 3′ 2⅜″, is spanned by each hip, and is stepped up upon the pattern with 17 and 15, the hip-pitch figures. These two hips are cut and pitched exactly like a pair of rafters, except that the plumb cut at plate throat will carry the hip splay. The angle hip matches the two wall hips, except that an inch must be sliced off its plumb cut to make it right in length. We have the three alternative methods for the hip cuts. We may make the wall hips pitch to meet each other, cutting back the front hip as with the complete turret. We may cut all three hips right and left handed to splay together at the top joint, or we may cut all three hips square through, adjusting the difference in length with a solid square finial block, in width equal to thickness of the hip stuff. In either case the part-roof employed upon the square-angle bay may be in exact duplicate of the whole roof which was used upon the complete turret.

TURRETS AND BAYS OF UNEVEN PITCH

A square turret with sides of uneven pitch is shown next. Each pair of hips now pitches to one end of a level ridge. Using separate portions of this arrangement for bay roofs, we may perhaps need the single steep pitch to the front, or we may have the pair of sharp pitches at either side, according to the direction in which we may suppose our original roof to have been sliced. As with uneven pitches upon the main roofs, we begin by finding pitch figures for each face separately, and find that the front is of 14″ pitch, while the sharp sides rise 21″ in the foot. We commence figuring by bringing both run figures to agree with the same rise. Whether this rise figure is for the sharp or for the flat pitch is immaterial. If desired, we may keep to the foot of span upon the 21″ pitch, when the corresponding figure that now gives the run measurement for the flat pitch will be 18″. That is to say, the steep pitch rises 21″ in 12″, while the flat pitch rises to the same 21″ in an 18″ run. Or we may prefer to retain our foot of span upon the flat pitch with its 14″ rise figure. To find the run for this 14″ rise upon the sharp pitch, we set our square to the sharp pitch figures 21″ and 12″, we place a runner closely against the blade, and slide the square forward to this angle until the flat rise figure 14″ is seen upon the tongue. We can now read off 8″ from the tongue as run for the sharp pitch rafter when its rise is reduced to 14″. Then the flat pitch is now known to rise 14″ in its 12″ span, while the sharp pitch rises 14″ in an 8″ span. With these two rafter runs known, we measure off the diagonal distance between them for run of the hips or valleys. Setting to 12 and 8 upon the square, we make this measurement and find it to be about 14 5/12″. Then with 14 5/12, hip run, upon tongue, and 14, roof rise, upon blade, we have cuts for this pair of irregular hips. Every time that we step the square containing these figures up the pattern, we have laid off so much of the irregular hip length as corresponds to 1′ of our flat span. In place of stepping this measurement, we may take it off from the square at once as about 20¾″. Multiplying this 20¾″ by the number of feet in the rafter-span, gives us finished length for the irregular hips. If any fraction of a foot remains in the rafter span, we may obtain the corresponding hip length by a proportion sum upon the square. Measuring across the square from 14 5/12 to 14, we have 20¾″ of hip length, which corresponds to a flat rafter span of 12″. We may set the square to this pair of figures, press the blade firmly against a runner, and slide the square at this angle till any smaller span appears upon the tongue, when the corresponding hip length can be read off from the blade. Getting figures that will cut the flat and sharp hip splays, we set the square to the two rafter run figures, 12 and 8, and we slide the square at this angle till 14 5/12″, the hip run, is seen upon each arm in turn. Reading each time the figures found upon the opposite arms give us about 9 7/12 and 21 7/12. Then 20¾ hip length with 9 7/12 cuts the sharp hip splay, and the same 20¾ hip splay with 21 7/12 gives the blunt hip splay. Jack splays to the flat roof pitch are cut with flat rafter length, 18 7/16″ on blade, and sharp rafter run, 8″, on tongue. Setting the square to this bevel and sliding till spacing of the jack rafters on centres appears upon tongue, we may read off from blade the difference in lengths of successive jack rafters. Distance from 8″, the sharp rafter run, to 14, the rise figure, is about 16″, so 16″, the sharp rafter length, with 12″, the flat rafter run, supplies jack splays for the sharp pitch. Setting again to this bevel, we slide till the spacing of our jacks on centres appears upon the tongue, when difference in lengths of our jack rafters will be found upon blade.

ROOFING REGULAR OCTAGONS

With pitch of the roof and span of the rafter, we proceed to set out our rafter pattern. In a true octagon no rafters will actually be cut to this pattern, but it will be needed for lengths of the octagon jacks. As rafter length for our individual pitch upon blade with 12 upon tongue supplies jack splays for the roofs with square-angled plates, so the same rafter length for 1′ upon blade with 5 on tongue supplies splay figures that are correct for these octagon jack rafters. Roofing an octagon to the 16″ pitch, we find that rafter length for the foot of span is now 20″. Then 20 upon blade and 5 on tongue gives octagon jack splays that are correct for this particular pitch. By sliding or by figuring we discover variation in the lengths of successive octagon jack rafters. These jacks are known to differ 20″ in length for every 5″ of spacing. Then if 2″ jacks are to be set at 12″ spaces, which is 14″ on centres, we have 20″ of jack variation for the first 5″ of spacing, another 20″ of jack variation for the second 5″ in the spacing, and a final 16″ of variation for the odd 4″ in the spacing, making a total variation figure of 20 plus 20 plus 16, or 56″, equalling 4′ 8″, for a jack spacing consisting of 5 plus 5 plus 4, or 14″ centres. Octagon hips for this roof will be set out every bit as easily as we set out the jacks. We use 12 on tongue and 16 on blade to set out the rafters for a roof of the 16″ pitch. We simply change over to 13 upon tongue with the same 16 upon blade to get cuts that are correct for the octagon hip or valley of the 16″ pitch. When using the foot-span system, in every roof the rafter and jack cuts are given by 12 on tongue and the rise in 1′ upon the blade. In every case the octagon hip or valley is set out with 13 upon tongue and the same rise for 1′ upon the blade. Stepping these figures up the pattern or measuring off the distance between them gives length of the octagon hip for every foot of rafter span, in this case about 20⅝″. We step or measure off this distance so many times as 1′ is contained in the rafter span. To get value of the hip length for any odd fraction of a foot in this span we set the square to 12 and 20⅝, and slide at this bevel till the required span is shown upon the tongue, when correct distance to measure off along the octagon hip will be found on blade. We may choose to treat the hip abutments for this octagonal turret in any of the ways that have been shown for hips to the square turret. Two hips at opposite angles may be allowed to span the whole diagonal distance and meet each other point to point. In this case the second pair pitched across from opposite angles standing square from the first will now rest upon the sides of this first pair, and must each be cut back by half their thickness. The last four octagonal hips may then be splayed to right and left to fit the square angles so produced. Or again, we may choose to cut all eight hips with splays to right and left, and the eight identical hips will all pitch together. If it is desired to avoid splays to these octagon hips we may cut square through to the octagon plumb cut, and pitch all eight hips against an eight-square or octagonal finial.

OCTAGONAL ROOFWORK ON IRREGULAR PITCHES

We next outline a roof that is accurate as to the octagon angle, but irregular in the lengths of its sides. Inspection will show that this is only the roof last dealt with, but now with a short length of straight roofing inserted. It differs from the last example, first in necessity for cutting the required number of main rafters, and next in the fact that both rafters and hips will now pitch against the ridge. Sometimes one end may be sliced from a roof of this last form to provide covering for a bay employing five sides from the regular octagon. But the methods which are sufficient to roof the whole octagon very obviously will be competent to roof any part required, and we have only to omit such portions of the whole roof as are not called for.

But the bay or cant window that employs only three sides from the octagon is more common, and its roof again is nothing but a slice from one or other of the octagon roofs last shown. A ridge will be fixed to the wall, and distance from plumb of this ridge face to plumb of the plate face gives the span of our rafter. With span and pitch known we may measure off or step out our pattern. Fractions in the span may be measured square out from the last complete foot mark on the pattern rafter, or may be had as before by sliding upon the square. Changing over to 13 on tongue, we step out the octagon hip, making the same number of steps that have been made upon the rafter pattern, and thus giving the same number of feet in the span. Fractions in the span may be turned into fractional hip lengths as before by sliding upon the square. The figures that step up the octagon hip, 13 on tongue and rise for the foot span on blade, will also set out the octagon plumb and seat cuts. Distance across the square between these points is length of the octagon hip for 1' of rafter span. This octagon hip length is used upon blade to mark off octagon hip splays to the ridge, while 13 is used on tongue. Octagon jack lengths are set out upon the rafter pattern exactly as before, and their splays again are cut with rafter length on blade and 5 on tongue. Wall hips to the octagon bay are simply true square-angled hips, and are therefore set out and cut to lengths and bevels with 17 upon tongue and rafter rise on blade.

Sometimes a roof may be employed which is true to the octagon angle, but varies in lengths of alternate sides, producing the irregular octagon with irregular pitches. A typical example is shown finally. Plates measure 8' across, of which 5' is length of the longer side. The roof is of the 18″ pitch upon these long sides. Since there is a measurement of 8' over plates, the pattern rafter will necessarily have a span of 4'. We set the square to 12 and 18, and step it up the pattern to this bevel four times, obtaining lengths and bevels for the pattern rafter. Or we may measure off this diagonal distance directly from the square as about $21\frac{5}{8}$″, and can then lay off the result along the timber by direct measurement.

We shall next require lengths of the hip runs. Distance spanned by the rafter is known to be 4'. Distance from arris of the plate angle to plate centre is 2' 6″ or 30″. Then in running directly inward by 4', our hip runs sideways by 30″, which works out to $7\frac{1}{2}$″ in one foot of rafter span. Immediately we know that the jack splays upon the long plate are cut by 21⅝ on blade and 7½ on tongue. Since this roof is of irregular pitch, so also the octagon jack splays become irregular. Jack variation is obtained either by sliding from these figures, or arithmetically. Measuring across the square from 12 to 7½, we have run for the irregular octagon hip as about 14 2/12. Then setting to 14 2/12 on tongue and to 18 on blade, we have plumb and seat cuts for the hips. Stepping this pair of figures four times supplies full finished lengths for these irregular octagonal hips. Lengths are next needed for the jack rafters of flatter pitch that rest upon the shorter plate. Had the distance to centre been alike upon all sides, the roof would have been of even pitch and one rafter could be used throughout, but with different runs we have a different pitch and different rafter, which has next to be set out. If a square of 8′ sides were being roofed, plainly the rafter run would be 4′, and the diagonal run four times 17″, or 5′ 8″. But the short octagonal plate cuts off a corner from this complete square, and therefore reduces the diagonal run in proportion. We know the complete square to be of 8′ sides, of which 5′ is occupied by the long plate, leaving 3′ of the complete square to be occupied by both of the diagonal angle plates, or 18″ for each. Then these two plates each stand upon the diagonal of a square with 18″ sides. By measurement of figuring we find that their length is 2′ 1½″. Then the diagonal plate sets back by half its length, or 1′ 0¾″ from the angle of the complete 8′ square. We deduct 1′ 0¾″, the run from angle of the square to face of the diagonal plate, from 5′ 8″, which is the diagonal run for the whole 4′ rafter, and get 4′ 7¼″ as distance from face of short plate to centre of the roof. This 4′ 7¼″ is evidently the run figure for the rafter that rests upon this short diagonal plate. We may take the whole rafter run with the whole rafter rise to get rafter length and cuts, or can use the foot-run rise and reduce the rafter-run figure to its foot-span equivalent. There are 4′ of span in the main rafter, so we divide by four, getting 1′ 1 13/16″ as run of this rafter in one foot of main span. Setting to 13 13/16 on tongue and rafter length on blade, we mark off plumb and seat cuts for these jack rafters. Distance between these points is about 22¾″, and is value of this rafter for one foot of the main span. We can multiply by four to get finished rafter length as 3′ 11″, or can set the square to 13 13/16 and 18, and step these figures four times up the pattern. Distance from point to centre of this short plate is already known as 1′ 0¾″, and full rafter length with full plate run, 3′ 11″ and 1′ 0¾″, supplies the irregular octagon jack splays for this flat pitch. Using foot-span figures we divide plate run by four, since there are four feet of span in this 1′ 0¾″ of plate run, and get 3 3/16″. Then 22¾ and 3 3/16 supplies the jack-splay figures required.

Sometimes a roof of this type will be used with a run of straight rafters inserted in its longer sides. The required number of rafters must then be cut to the pattern and pitched against a ridge. With the ridge in place, our hips will now splay against it. Once more a half-slice from this last type is sometimes employed to terminate bay-windows that have been carried through two floors, but the man who is capable of carrying out the whole roof will find no added difficulty in dealing with one half.

ROOFING HEXAGONS AND THE REGULAR POLYGONS

Square bays are considered too angular by many architects, who object to the limited room space that is afforded by the old octagon bay with its wings set at the 45° angle. The bay or oriel employing five sides from the octagon is a useful alternative that has already been shown, but still other treatments are available if the bay angle is changed and the number of sides is increased or diminished. The hexagon or 60° angle gives a bay with more internal accommodation than the 45° octagonal figure, and is very frequently employed. Questions of cost will usually rule out the true circular bay which was employed so liberally in the days of cheap labour, but very creditable circular effects can be produced with a succession of straight casements resting upon brickwork that is circular in plan. These straight lights set around a circular outline, of course constitute a regular polygon. To cut window-boards, seats, skirting, architrave or roofs to a bay, oriel or turret with any given number of sides, we may turn to the Polygon Table on page 184, Vol. II, and look out its mitre angle. To give cutting figures that will cover wide material, these mitres are calculated to a 24″ base, but by halving both sides as we take them from this table we shall get figures that are correct to the foot of span. Roofing one of the popular hexagon bays we take out 24 and 13 10/12ths as the figures that cut its mitre, and by halving both sides we have 12 and 6 11/12ths. Then for every foot that the hexagon rafter and hip run square in from their plate, the hexagon hip runs 6 11/12ths to one side. At once we have rafter length and 6 11/12ths, as figures that cut these hexagon jack splays. Taking a roof of the 16″ pitch for illustration, the hexagon jack splays are cut by 20 and 6 11/12ths, and so for every other polygon that is given in this table. As before, we get the jack variation by sliding from these figures or arithmetically. Hexagon hip run is the diagonal distance from 12 to 6 11/12ths, and is measured off across the square as about 13 7/8ths. Then 13 7/8ths hexagon hip run, with 16, rafter rise, gives plumb and seat cuts for the hexagon hip rafter.

Roofing a polygon with any other number of sides, we first look out its mitre angle from the Polygon Table. The figures given in this table are already correct for a roof of 2′ span, and to find the figures for the foot of span we divide by two. Finding the pitch of our roof gives us rafter length for the foot of span, and this rafter length with the mitre figure for one foot from the table supplies jack splays for the chosen polygon. By figuring or by sliding we convert these jack-splay figures into figures showing the jack variation for our chosen spacing. We measure across the square from 12 to the mitre figure for one foot to get run of the polygonal hip, and with hip run and roof pitch we may set out the hips for any chosen polygon accurately to lengths and bevels.

Square-angled, polygonal and irregular roofs have now been illustrated. Even pitches and irregular intersections have been dealt with. The steel square has been shown in use from the basement excavations to the turret roofs. Still its possibilities are not exhausted, for every day the steel-square men are carrying their tool ahead to untried work. In due course the present reader may supply his contribution. The old uncertain bevel-board has become a clumsy and expensive joke, and steel-square men everywhere exchange accurate bevel cuts in inches. Our old familiar inch measurements found upon the square now lay off every building bevel as readily and as accurately as they mark off widths and lengths. But the steel-square methods that offer command over space will also control time. The old-time joiners who fitted their wooden bevel moulds into existing spaces had to wait until the space had been made before it could be fitted, but a roof of 16″ pitch is settled as of 16″ pitch from the instant that it is delineated by the architect, and can be cut from that moment irrespective of building progress. Wing-light dormers that fit above this roof slope, cupboard fronts that stand beneath it, and all similar items of joinery are also of the 16″ pitch from the moment that the architect determines it. Forethought is introduced into woodworking methods, all work proceeds simultaneously, and building, roof and joinery all agree when finally assembled.

CHAPTER II

FRAME CONSTRUCTION

Construction Data—Formulæ for computing Strength of Wooden Beams—Construction—Modern Framing—Combined Framing—Framing of Plans—Floors in Framing—Floors—Shingle Roofs.

AMERICAN METHODS

OF recent times considerable energy has been expended in a search for new methods of construction, particularly as applied to Housing. The main object of this research has been to discover, if possible, some form of construction which, though it may not have the same durability and strength as bricks and masonry, yet shall have these qualities in a degree sufficient for buildings of a sufficiently permanent type to meet the needs of the present urgency and which shall be less expensive and quicker to build.

Of all the new forms which have been investigated, there does not appear any which, in the last two requirements, surpasses wooden frame building such as has been practised in America since the days of early colonisation. It is agreed that the need is a temporary one which will pass off with increased construction so long only as it is quick, when a return may be made to the older and more permanent forms. It is not in any way intended that any new form which may be discovered shall permanently oust brick, masonry, or concrete.

Consequently, seeing that this is so, the fullest consideration should be given to that type of building in which houses were erected at the time of the early settlement of the American colonies, and where buildings over 100 years old are still standing occupied to-day. The durability of frame construction may be said to have been proved, whereas that of some of the newer inventions is still a matter of uncertainty, and of the saving in cost there can be no doubt. So far as time is concerned, where claims are put forward for new forms of construction that houses can be erected like Jack's beanstalk during the night, it would be unwise to offer any claim for a comparison between any form of real building construction with the astounding results to be obtained from the waving of magicians' wands. The subject is a serious one, and worthy of serious investigation.

Certain doubts, which at first sight may have seemed reasonable, have been expressed as to the supply of timber ; and the closing of the Baltic ports at the time when these doubts were expressed, no doubt gave additional justification for the fear. However, as exportation from these ports has been recommenced, and a proper realisation of the size and possibilities of the North American forests has yet to become general, it may prove upon enquiry that this—the most serious objection raised against a general adoption of American frame building in this country—has no real weight.

The provinces of Quebec, Ontario, British Columbia and part of Alberta are each over three times the size of the Canadian lakes, and the Canadian lakes, taken together, cover a greater area than England and Scotland.

Comprehensive surveys have been completed only for the provinces of Nova Scotia and British Columbia—an inventory of the forest resources of Ontario is being completed and extensive areas of forest land have been examined in the three prairie provinces ; but the information is still incomplete as to the total resources of these provinces. For several years a thorough survey of the Crown lands and New Brunswick has been in process, and about 60 per cent. of these lands have been covered. As yet only a relatively small portion of the forest area of Quebec has been reported on. Approximately one-quarter of the land area of Canada is forest land, being 950,000 square miles, less than half of this carrying timber of merchantable size at the present time, and about a quarter carrying timber of 10" in diameter.

A table from the Forestry Report of the Department of the Interior of Canada is given below, and shows the estimated stand of timber of merchantable size in Canada by regions so far as the survey has proceeded :

Region.	Saw material.		Pulpwood, Cordwood, Posts, etc.	
	1,000 ft. B.M.	1,000 c. ft.	1,000 cords.	1,000 c. ft.
Softwood :				
Eastern Provinces . . .	76,101,000	16,666,115	552,210	64,700,590
Prairie Provinces . . .	17,985,000	3,938,715	272,010	31,825,170
British Columbia . . .	345,762,000	75,721,878	47,500	5,557,500
Total	439,848,000	96,326,708	871,720	10,208,326
Hardwood :				
Eastern Provinces . . .	32,134,500	7,037,430	209,815	20,342,417
Prairie Provinces . . .	9,305,000	2,037,795	196,010	18,620,950
British Columbia . . .	788,000	172,572	2,160	205,200
Total	42,227,500	9,247,797	407,985	39,168,567
Grand Total . . .	482,075,500	105,574,505	1,279,705	141,251,827

Of the Northern Provinces perhaps no man knows the timber resources exactly, and certainly few can realise the immensity thereof. Canada's forests are estimated to comprise 800 billion feet of commercial timber and 1 billion cords of pulp wood, and, as all that is required for the present

FIG. 3.—MODERN HALF-TIMBERING, BARGE BOARDS AND WOOD CARVING.
Architects, Edwin T. Hall, F.R.I.B.A., F.R.San.I., and E. Stanley Hall, M.A., F.R.I.B.A.

need is to build temporary accommodation, clearly there will be no shortage of timber until long after our needs are satisfied.

The fear that the supply of timber will not prove equal to a much larger demand than our present need, which, it must be remembered, is merely a temporary one, is therefore without foundation.

Of other objections raised against frame construction, that of doubt as to strength and firmness is more often felt than openly expressed. No doubt the reason for this disinclination to give expression to the view originates from the same cause as the view itself, which can be only lack of knowledge and experience. For, though a drawing of a frame building, and even the building itself in course of construction, may give an impression of something too slender even beyond the limits of jerry building, yet, to anyone who has lived many years in all seasons and the various climates to be met with throughout America and Canada, there can be no uncertainty that a frame building provides as firm and strong a building, and one in every way as comfortable to live in, as any other form of construction yet devised. There is less conductivity about a frame building than any other, and consequently less loss of heat in cold weather ; also, if properly constructed, there should be no such thing as damp either from percolation or condensation. It must be confessed, and should be acknowledged, that the objections to frame building on these grounds are prejudice, and not based on fact, but arise rather from an unaccustomedness on the part of the eye, grown used for generations to an exhibition of strength on the part of the materials used in building far in excess of that which is actually required. An interesting calculation might be made of the total amount of force wasted in the excess of strength of brick walls over the actual weight they are required to carry ; and a great future might be found to be before the inventor who could turn that latent energy into an active and useful force.

To one who has built and lived in frame buildings, not only houses, but larger buildings, such as apartment buildings and offices, none of the objections raised against the method carry any weight at all. Frame buildings are as satisfactory as any other, provided that proper construction suited to the material is employed.

Consequently it is felt that some account of the method of construction of frame buildings as employed in America will be useful, especially at the present time, when, for purposes of Housing at least, some of the more restrictive by-laws which have prevented, amongst other things, frame building, are to be either rescinded or waived.

In this matter of building by-laws it may well be that the chief obstruction against the use of frame construction has lain ; for, as a matter of fact, it was employed in some form in England long before it appeared in America, the only difference being that in its country of adoption custom has reduced the dimensions of its component parts and also relied upon the framework only, without the filling-in material customary in the country of its origin. And herein may lie the real

cause of its rejection as a general method of construction. By-laws
were originally framed as much as protective measures against the
spread of fire as for any other reason ; and this, where houses are crowded
together on the land is, of course, a matter of very serious importance.
However, as in the modern housing scheme, restrictive measures are
taken limiting the number of houses per acre, the same restrictions with
regard to the material that may be employed in their construction would
not seem to be necessary. There is naturally not the same fear of fire
spreading amongst houses which are built some distance apart as amongst
those built touching or almost touching. Also, with the spread of
knowledge in fireproofing methods, framework may be covered with
materials such as asbestos sheeting, which renders them quite as fireproof
as the roof of a masonry building covered with tiles or slates.

CONSTRUCTION DATA

MEASUREMENT OF LUMBER.—Lumber of all kinds in America is sold
in 10', 12', 14' and 16' lengths, and, as lengths between these dimensions
must be cut to waste, these lengths should be borne in mind by the
designer, if this can be done without unduly cramping his design.

AVERAGE ULTIMATE CRUSHING LOADS IN POUNDS, FOR AMERICAN TIMBERS

Material—Woods (Endways).	Crushing weight in lbs. per sq. inch.
Cedar	3,500
Chestnut	4,000
Cypress	3,375
Hemlock	3,000
Oak, white	4,000
Pine, Georgia yellow	5,000
Pine, Oregon	4,500
Pine, Norway	3,800
Pine, white	3,500
Pine (Colorado)	3,150
Redwood (California)	3,000
Spruce	4,000
Whitewood	3,000

The strength of a *wooden column* or strut may be found from the
following rule : where the length is not more than twelve times the least
thickness, the safe load equals the area of the cross section multiplied
by the strength of the material as given in the table divided by the factor
of safety.

The strength of a column, post, or strut depends in a large measure
upon the proportion of the length to the diameter, or the least thickness.
Up to a certain length failure occurs due to compression only, and above
that length first by bending and then by breaking. The factor of safety
depends upon the position in which the column or strut is to be housed,
the load which comes upon it and the quality of the material. For
timber of ordinary quality a factor of safety of 5 is recommended, which
means that one-eighth of the figures given in the table be used.

For example, if it is desired to find the safe load for an oak post 8″ by 8″ by 10′ 0″ long, using a factor of safety area of cross-section equals 64 sq. ins. ; safe load per sq. in. equals $\frac{4000}{5}$ equals 800 ; 800 × 64 equals 51,200 lbs. *Wood Posts over 12 diameters in length*, being liable to bend under the load, are correspondingly liable to break under a less load than would a shorter column of the same cross-section. The formula given in Kidder's *Handbook*, devised by Mr. James H. Stanwood for yellow pine posts, is as follows :

Safe load per square inch equals 1000–10 by $\dfrac{\text{length in ins.}}{\text{breadth in ins.}}$

For Texas pine, oak and white pine posts, the following formula is given :

Safe load per square inch equals 850–8·5 by $\dfrac{\text{length in ins.}}{\text{breadth in ins.}}$

For oak and Norway pine :

Safe load per square inch equals 750–7·5 by $\dfrac{\text{length in ins.}}{\text{breadth in ins.}}$

And for white pine and spruce posts :

Safe load per square inch equals 625–6 by $\dfrac{\text{length in ins.}}{\text{breadth in ins.}}$

In all of which the breadth is the least side or the diameter of a circular post.

SAFE LOAD IN POUNDS FOR YELLOW PINE AND OREGON PINE POSTS (ROUND AND SQUARE)

Size of Post in inches.	Length of Post in feet.								
	8	10	12	14	15	16	18	20	24
4 × 6 .	18,200	16,800	15,360						
5½ round .	19,590	18,760	17,550	16,500					
6 × 6 .	30,200	28,800	27,400	25,900	25,200	24,500			
6 × 8 .	40,300	38,400	36,500	34,600	33,600	32,600			
6 × 10 .	50,400	48,000	45,600	43,200	42,000	40,800			
7½ round .	38,540	37,130	35,710	34,300	33,590	32,890			
8 × 8 .	64,000	54,400	52,500	50,600	49,600	48,600	46,700		
8 × 10 .	80,000	68,000	65,600	63,200	62,000	60,800	53,400		
8 × 12 .	96,000	81,600	78,700	76,800	74,400	73,000	70,100		
9½ round .	70,900	61,970	60,190	58,350	57,429	56,580	54,800		
10 × 10 .	100,000	100,000	85,600	83,200	82,000	80,800	78,400	76,000	
10 × 12 .	120,000	120,000	102,700	99,800	98,400	87,000	94,100	91,200	
10 × 14 .	140,000	140,000	119,800	116,500	114,800	113,100	109,800	106,400	
11½ round .	103,900	103,900	90,912	88,730	87,690	86,500	84,160	82,290	
12 × 12 .	144,000	144,000	144,000	123,800	122,400	121,000	118,100	115,200	109,440
12 × 14 .	168,000	168,000	168,000	144,500	142,800	141,100	137,800	134,400	127,680
12 × 16 .	192,000	192,000	192,000	165,100	163,200	161,300	157,400	153,600	145,920
14 × 14 .	196,000	196,000	196,000	196,000	170,900	169,100	165,800	162,400	155,800
16 × 16 .	256,000	256,000	256,000	256,000	229,100	225,300	221,400	217,600	209,900
18 × 18 .	324,000	324,000	324,000	324,000	324,000	289,400	285,100	280,800	272,160
20 × 20 .	400,000	400,000	400,000	400,000	400,000	400,000	356,800	352,000	342,400

SAFE LOAD FOR TEXAS (YELLOW) PINE POSTS (ROUND AND SQUARE)

Size of Post in inches.	Length of Post in feet.								
	8	10	12	14	15	16	18	20	24
4 × 6 .	15,500	14,280	13,050						
5½ round .	16,650	15,790	14,900	14,030					
6 × 6 .	25,704	24,480	23,256	22,032	21,420	20,808			
6 × 8 .	34,272	32,640	31,008	29,376	28,560	27,744			
6 × 10 .	42,840	40,800	37,760	36,720	35,700	34,680			
7½ round .	32,740	31,540	30,340	29,140	28,540	27,940	26,740		
8 × 8 .	47,870	46,240	44,600	42,970	42,160	41,340	39,710		
8 × 10 .	59,840	57,800	55,760	53,720	52,700	51,680	49,640		
8 × 12 .	71,808	69,360	66,910	64,460	63,240	62,000	59,560		
9½ round .	54,150	52,650	51,150	49,580	48,820	49,070	46,570		
10 × 10 .	85,000	78,800	72,760	70,720	69,700	68,680	66,640	64,600	
10 × 12 .	102,000	89,760	87,300	84,860	83,640	82,400	80,000	77,500	
10 × 14 .	119,000	104,700	101,860	99,000	97,580	96,150	93,300	90,400	
11½ round .	88,290	79,100	77,250	75,400	74,470	73,550	71,700	69,850	66,160
12 × 12 .	122,400	110,160	107,700	105,260	104,040	102,800	100,360	97,920	93,000
12 × 14 .	142,800	128,520	125,660	122,800	121,380	119,950	117,100	114,240	108,520
12 × 16 .	163,200	146,880	143,600	140,350	138,720	137,080	133,800	130,560	124,030
14 × 14 .	166,600	166,600	149,450	146,600	145,180	143,760	140,900	138,080	132,400
14 × 16 .	190,400	190,400	170,800	167,500	165,900	164,300	161,000	157,800	151,300
16 × 16 .	217,600	217,600	217,600	194,700	193,000	191,400	188,200	184,900	178,400

SAFE LOAD IN POUNDS FOR OAK AND NORWAY PINE POSTS (ROUND AND SQUARE)

Size of Post in inches.	Length of Post in feet.								
	8	10	12	14	15	16	18	20	24
4 × 6 .	13,680	12,600	11,520						
5½ round .	14,700	13,900	13,160	12,370					
6 × 6 .	22,680	21,600	20,520	19,440	18,900	18,360			
6 × 8 .	30,240	28,800	27,360	25,920	25,200	24,480			
6 × 10 .	37,800	36,000	34,200	32,400	31,500	30,600			
7½ round .	28,900	27,850	26,780	25,720	25,190	24,660			
8 × 8 .	42,240	40,768	39,360	37,880	37,120	36,480	35,000		
8 × 10 .	52,800	50,960	49,200	47,360	46,400	44,600	43,760		
8 × 12 .	63,360	61,152	59,040	56,830	55,680	54,720	52,500		
9½ round .	47,960	46,440	45,160	43,740	43,100	42,400	41,120		
10 × 10 .	75,000	66,000	64,200	62,400	61,500	60,600	58,800	57,000	
10 × 12 .	90,000	79,200	77,040	74,880	73,800	72,720	70,560	68,400	
10 × 14 .	105,000	92,400	89,880	87,360	86,100	84,840	82,320	79,800	
11½ round .	77,925	69,820	68,160	66,490	65,770	64,833	63,170	61,600	
12 × 12 .	108,000	108,000	95,040	92,880	91,700	90,700	88,560	86,400	82,080
12 × 14 .	126,000	126,000	110,800	108,300	107,000	105,840	103,300	100,802	95,760
12 × 16 .	144,000	144,000	126,700	123,800	122,300	120,900	118,000	115,200	109,400
14 × 14 .	147,000	147,000	147,000	129,300	128,100	127,000	124,400	121,900	116,800
16 × 16 .	192,000	192,000	192,000	192,000	170,500	168,900	166,100	163,000	157,400
18 × 18 .	243,000	243,000	243,000	243,000	243,000	217,000	213,800	210,600	204,100
20 × 20 .	300,000	300,000	300,000	300,000	300,000	300,000	267,600	254,000	256,000

SAFE LOAD IN POUNDS FOR WHITE PINE AND SPRUCE POSTS (ROUND AND SQUARE)

Size of Post in inches.	Length of Post in feet.								
	8	10	12	14	15	16	18	20	24
4 × 6 .	11,520	10,550	9,800	8,700					
5½ round .	12,350	11,730	11,180	10,490					
6 × 6 .	19,080	18,216	17,352	16,490	16,050	15,620			
6 × 8 .	25,440	24,290	23,140	21,980	21,400	20,830			
6 × 10 .	31,800	30,360	28,920	27,480	26,760	26,040			
7½ round .	24,220	23,380	22,540	21,660	21,260	20,820			
8 × 8 .	35,450	34,300	33,150	32,000	31,420	30,850	29,700		
8 × 10 .	44,320	42,480	41,440	40,000	39,280	38,560	37,120		
8 × 12 .	53,180	51,450	49,730	48,000	47,140	46,270	44,544		
9½ round .	40,000	39,000	37,860	36,800	36,230	35,730	34,670		
10 × 10 .	62,500	55,400	53,960	52,520	51,800	51,080	49,640	48,200	
10 × 12 .	75,000	66,480	64,800	63,000	62,160	61,300	59,570	57,840	
10 × 14 .	87,500	77,560	75,600	73,500	72,520	71,510	69,500	67,480	
11½ round .	64,930	58,390	57,140	55,800	55,170	54,550	53,100	51,950	
12 × 12 .	90,000	90,000	79,780	78,000	77,180	76,320	74,590	72,860	69,400
12 × 14 .	105,000	105,000	93,170	91,050	90,050	89,000	87,020	85,000	80,900
12 × 16 .	120,000	120,000	106,300	104,000	102,900	101,700	99,400	97,150	92,500
14 × 14 .	122,500	122,500	110,350	108,350	107,400	106,400	104,460	102,300	98,400
16 × 16 .	160,000	160,000	160,000	143,870	142,590	141,570	139,260	136,960	132,366
18 × 18 .	202,500	202,500	202,500	202,500	183,060	181,760	179,170	176,580	171,400
20 × 20 .	250,000	250,000	250,000	250,000	250,000	250,000	250,000	224,500	221,200	215,200

The following rules are taken from Kidder's *Architect's and Builder's Pocket Book* :

FORMULÆ FOR COMPUTING STRENGTH OF WOODEN BEAMS

For Beams fixed at one end and loaded at the other :

The safe load in lbs. $= \dfrac{\text{breadth} \times \text{square of depth} \times x}{4 \times \text{length in feet.}}$

Breadth in ins. $= \dfrac{4 \times \text{load} \times \text{length in feet}}{\text{square of depth} \times x}$.

For Beams fixed at one end loaded with a uniformly distributed load :

The safe load in lbs. $= \dfrac{\text{breadth} \times \text{square of depth} \times x}{2 \times \text{length in feet}}$.

Breadth in ins. $= \dfrac{2 \times \text{load} \times \text{length in feet}}{\text{square of depth} \times x}$.

For Beams supported at both ends and loaded in the middle :

The safe load in lbs. $= \dfrac{\text{breadth} \times \text{square of depth} \times x}{\text{span in feet}}$.

Breadth in ins. $= \dfrac{\text{span in feet} \times \text{load}}{\text{square of depth} \times x}$.

For Beams supported at both ends with load uniformly distributed :

The safe load in lbs. $= \dfrac{2 \times \text{breadth} \times \text{square of depth} \times x}{\text{span in feet}}$.

$$\text{Breadth in ins.} = \frac{\text{span in feet} \times \text{load}}{2 \times \text{square of depth} \times x}.$$

Beams supported at both ends and loaded with a concentrated load not over the centre :

$$\text{The safe load in lbs.} = \frac{\text{breadth} \times \text{square of depth} \times \text{span} \times x}{4 \times m \times n}.$$

Where m = the major distance of load from support.

„ n = the minor   „   „   „   „

$$\text{Breadth in ins.} = \frac{4 \times \text{load} \times m \times n}{\text{square of depth} \times \text{span} \times x}.$$

Beams supported at both ends and loaded with w pounds at two points equidistant (m) from each supported end.

$$\left.\begin{array}{c}\text{The safe load } w \text{ in}\\ \text{lbs. at each point}\end{array}\right\} = \frac{\text{breadth} \times \text{square of depth} \times x}{4 \times m}.$$

$$\text{Breadth in ins.} = \frac{4 \times \text{load at one point} \times m}{\text{square of depth} \times x}.$$

VALUES OF X—CO-EFFICIENT FOR BEAMS

Material.	x lbs.	Material.	x lbs.
Chestnut	60	Pine, white, Eastern . . .	60
Hemlock	55	„ „ Western . . .	65
Oak, white	75	„ Texas, yellow . . .	90
Pine, Georgia, yellow . . .	100	Spruce	70
„ Oregon . . .	90	Whitewood (Poplar) . . .	65
„ red, or Norway . . .	70	Redwood (California) . . .	60

WEIGHT.—For any given class of timber of a given condition the strength is directly proportional to its weight. The strongest portion of a young tree is the heart, and the upper portion of a tree is slightly weaker than the lower. Older trees are stronger midway between the heart and the sap.

KNOTS.—Large knots weaken timber equally in tension as in compression, and timber having these to any great extent should be rejected.

SEASONING.—All kinds of timber are about twice as strong when thoroughly seasoned as they are in the green state, and in the U.S. timber tests it is stated that it has also been shown that the maximum strength corresponds to about 5 or 6 per cent. moisture, the strength at absolute dryness being somewhat reduced.

CLASS OF AMERICAN TIMBER

CHOICE OF TIMBERS.—For framing timbers woods which can be obtained in large dimensions, and are abundant and cheap, are chosen where ordinary weights are to be supported ; though, where additional strength is required, the choice becomes limited to those of the hardwood types.

The following list gives the main classes of timber used for the various requirements of buildings in frame construction :

Type of Purpose.	Timber.
Light framing for houses, apartments, etc.	Spruce, white pine, Northern yellow pine, and hemlock.
Posts, girders and heavy framing	Southern pine, Canadian red pine, Norway pine, Spruce " Best."
Long truss timbers	Oregon and Georgia pine.
Posts and sleepers below ground	White cedar, chestnut, redwood, cypress.
Piles	Oak, Elm, Southern hard pine, Oregon pine, Norway pine spruce, cypress, hemlock, and white pine.
Floors	White oak, maple, Georgia pine.
Roofing shingles	Redwood cedar, cypress and white pine.
Doors and windows	White pine.
Interior finish	All hardwoods and redwood, cypress and white pine.

CONSTRUCTION

The origin of the lighter type of framing in use in America to-day, and known as *balloon framing*, was doubtless the half-timbering in vogue in England at that time, and carried across by the earlier settlers of the American colonies.   Examples are still to be seen in the Southern States, where the posts and beams are of hewn timbers from 8″ to 12″ square. The method is expressive of the days when labour was cheap and no mental restrictions were caused to the builders by reason of a fear of timber shortage or a too close study of requisite strengths.   The timbers were cut to lengths and framed together on the site one story at a time, all being mortised and pinned together.   And, whereas in England they were filled in with brickwork or plaster, in the new country they were covered with rough sheeting.   The work had an artistic charm which cannot be obtained by the lighter and more modern work, mainly owing to the fact that the beams and main posts being of greater thickness than the walls and floors projected into the interiors of the rooms, and, as these were often timbers roughly squared with the adze, a more natural appearance was thus contributed to the buildings at least internally in the new country, and both internally and externally in the old.

No doubt many of the oldest buildings—homesteads on earliest settlements—were formed of solid logs piled one on top of the other, with their ends halved and overlapping, as in fact they still are to-day in lumber camps and districts where the supply of timber is over-abundant.   In the same way fences to fields are still formed of split rails laid in a herringbone or zigzag pattern on top of the other, with their ends overlapping. Such fences are to be seen throughout Eastern Canada on settlements in timbered land where the clearing away of trees is the first object of the settler and the disposal of the cleared timber a matter of urgency.   The best that can be said for the method is that it is one step less wasteful

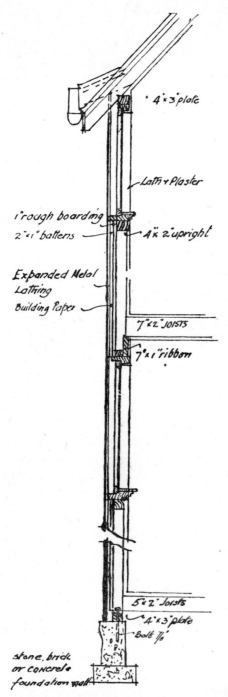

FIG. 4.—SECTION OF FRAME
BUILDING.

4" x 3" plate

Lath + Plaster

1" rough boarding

2" x 1" battens

4" x 2" upright

Expanded Metal
Lathing

Building Paper

7" x 2" joists

7" x 1" ribbon

5" x 2" joists

4" x 3" plate

Bolt 7/8

stone, brick
or concrete
foundation wall

than burning the timber, which is not unknown even in these days of fears of a timber shortage and reafforestation schemes.

Though the half-timbering with brick or plaster filling has much to make it preferable to us from an artistic standpoint, yet to early settlers where timbers were sawn at best by hand, and roughly leaving many outer slabs, these naturally supplied, ready to hand, the outer covering of the supporting timbers, from which there is no doubt the method of sheeting with clap board and shingles sprang.

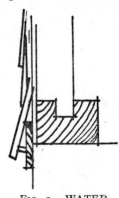

FIG. 5.—WATER
TABLE.

MODERN FRAMING

The type of framing used in modern work, known as Balloon Framing, is of a much lighter and less expensive form. A sill of from 6″ to 12″ by 4″ to 6″ is first laid on and bolted to the foundation walls, being half at the angles, and in its length if the latter is necessary, and pinned with wood pins or nailed at the halving. On these sills the floor joists are laid with the ends lining with the outer edge of the sill. Or alternatively the sill may be projected 1″ to 2″ from the ends of the joists

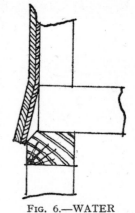

FIG. 6.—WATER
TABLE.

to form a tilter to the lower courses of sheeting, as shown in Fig. 6.

In this case the outer face of the sill should be cut splayed as shown to give a better fixing for the sheeting. The rough under flooring of good hemlock (spruce, native pine) boards, surfaced one side only, is next nailed to every bearing, with two nails to each joint. On the ground-floor and sometimes the upper stories also this boarding is laid diagonally. All end joints must be cut over a floor joist, and suitable nailing pieces are cut in between the joists at the side walls for the diagonal flooring. The edges of the flooring must be continued out to the outside sheeting. If a single floor only is desired, as is often the case with rooms in the roof, it is formed of 4″ clear spruce matched and secret nailed with heading joints cut over a bearing in every instance.

The next step is to erect the corner posts (Fig. 10), which may be either 4″ by 6″ single posts, or composed of two 4″ by 3″. Alternatively angle posts of a composite nature may be framed up, as shown in Fig. 25, p. 36, out of three 3″ by 3″ bolted together or two 4″ by 2″ bolted at right angles. Whatever form of corner post is adopted, it is essential that it should extend in one length from the sill to the plate from which the rafters spring. The corner posts may be tenoned to the sill, but are more often, in cheaper work, merely rested on their butt ends and nailed to the sills. When erected, these are stayed in position by boards nailed diagonally from sill to a point about half-way up their height. This stay in cheaper work is removed later, but in better-class work splaying halvings are cut out of the upright studs and a splayed notch is cut in the post to receive the splayed end of the stay. By this means the surfaces of the stay, studs and corner posts are all kept flush.

The positions of all door and window openings on all floors are next marked upon the sill, and against the outer edges of these openings double studs, two 4″ by 2″ nailed together, are raised. The spaces between these are then filled in with single studs, 4″ by 2″ in single lengths. These studs are temporarily kept in position by boards nailed from the corner posts to double studs on the inside. The feet of the studs are spiked to the sill. The height of the ceiling of the top-floor rooms less 3″ is then marked on the corner posts and lined off at right angles on all the double and intermediate studs. These are then cut to line. But as outside scaffolding, as we know it, is rarely used in the erection of frame buildings, the general practice is, as soon as all the studs are erected, a plank measuring 2″ by 7″ is notched into their inner faces at a height of 1″ above the ceiling of the ground-floor rooms ; the same is done if there are more than two stories at the necessary heights. This plan, which is called the *ribbon*, is of course required only along two opposite sides. On these, with their sides against and nailed to the upright studs, are spiked the floor joists; though, where more sound construction is desired, the floor joists are notched over the ribbons and nailed to the studs with three nails each. The rough under flooring is then laid and on this rough trestles support planks which give the necessary height to enable the studs to be cut to the desired lengths. When this is done two 2″ by 4″, one above the other, are nailed to the tops of the studs and corner posts. These form the plate on which the ceiling joists rest and over which the rafters are notched or bird's-mouthed according to the finish desired for the eaves. Where the plate is double, as described, halving is arranged at the angles, as shown in Fig. 7, but ending the upper place short by 4″ and running the upper plate at right angles in its place. This is the cheapest form of plate, but it is sometimes wished

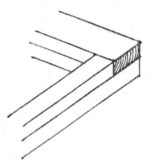

FIG. 7.—DOUBLE PLATE.

to have the plate above the joists, when an additional ribbon or ledger is cut in at the height desired, the studs being continued above this, and the plate nailed to their tops in the same manner as has been described. This enables a plate wider than the studs to be used if desired, as in the method already described the plate must be flush with the studs on the inside, leaving only the outside on which it may be projected, which is apt to cause inconvenience with the fixing of the outer wall covering. However, where the thrust from the rafters is great a wider wall plate is often necessary; but, whatever width is desired, it is best that it should be built up of 2″ pieces spiked together rather than that solid timbers should be used.

The heights of all door heads and window heads and sills are next marked on the studs between which they come, and short lengths of 2″ by 4″ studding nailed in, in double thicknesses. Underneath the window openings short lengths of studs are cut in and nailed to the double horizontal studding and the sill.

On the attic floor the joists should come on to the plate vertically over the upright studs, and the rafters should be nailed to their sides also.

COMBINATION FRAMING.—For better-class work a combination of the old half-timbering style and of that last described is used. The sills, posts and girts are treated in the same manner as in the

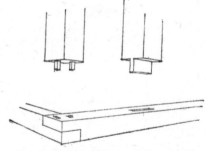

FIG. 8.—STUDDING AND PLATE.

balloon frame, but the studs are mortised at the lower end into the sill and cut off to lengths and spiked to the underside of a 4″ by 8″ girt fixed at the level of the underside of the floor joists. This 4″ by 8″ girt is mortised and pegged into a 4″ by 8″ corner post; and 3″ by 4″ angle braces let into the girt and the corner post act as braces. From a point two-thirds of the height of each story angle braces are also run from the corner post to the underside of the girt and plates; any studding coming against these is splay cut and nailed thereto above and below.

This method of framing should be employed for all larger buildings, including all houses larger than the cottage type.

NOTES.—When sills are cut for mortises it should be remembered that they are considerably weakened thereby, and if the sills do not rest on solid walls below, but upon piers or posts, the weight of the studs and floors above that opening have to be carried by the sills. It then becomes a question whether greater advantage is to be gained by thickening the sill and mortising or by only spiking the butted ends of the studs. In any case where undersheeting is nailed on to the plate and the studs are fixed, as they should be, diagonally, there would not seem to be the same need for the mortising of the feet of the studs to the sill. Also the same is true with regard to notching for floor joists to which sills are sometimes subjected. When this is the case, together with the mortisings for the studs, unless the sill is a very wide one there is little more than half the timbers left at each point of cutting ; and as the studs are fixed at distances rarely more than 24″ from centre to centre it will be seen that a great deal of the timber of the sill is cut away in total. More frequently the studding is spaced 16″ centre to centre, and in the best work so close as 12″, which means that at every 10″ over half the sill is cut away. However, where mortising is desired it may be performed in either of the methods shown in Fig. 9, the latter method being preferred by some.

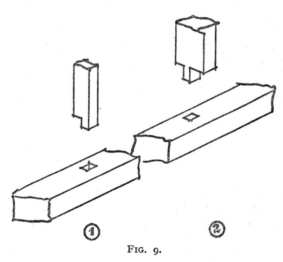

FIG. 9.

Studding for buildings of a size greater than the average house, such as apartment buildings, churches, etc., should be 2″ by 6″, in which case the corner posts need not of necessity be enlarged in proportion, but may come the same depth as the studding ; but to ensure a good nailing for the sheeting the corner post should always be 2″ wider one way than the other.

THE GIRT is the name given to that form of ribbon used in the combination framing last described. This may come either at the underside of the floor joist, in which case the floor joists will rest upon it ; or when running parallel to the floor joists, in which case the girt is fixed at the same height as the floor joists, when it is known as a *raised girt*. The joint between the post and girt is a splayed shoulder mortise pinned with a hardwood pin as shown in Fig. 12. And the joint between the brace and the post is similarly formed on the splay, Fig. 13. It should be remembered that braces are strongest when placed at an angle of 45°, and they should be connected to the post at a height of not less than one-third, and not more than one-half, the length of the post measured from floor to ceiling of one story.

FRAMING PLANS.—For the satisfactory and economical construction of a building to be erected in frame work, whilst it is not for one moment suggested that the framing should be allowed to influence the elevation to its detriment, yet the framework plans should be very carefully thought out and prepared in conjunction with the external elevation. In practice the best method to adopt is, having prepared the plans and elevations in the rough to lay over them tracing paper on which the skeleton of the framing only is drawn. By this method all openings will be properly cared for, and wherever possible framing of mill lengths will be used. In figuring framework plans it is customary to run the dimensions in every case from the centre to the centre of the timbers, and by this method common studding, in which there is much duplication, may be indicated by a single line. Also it should be noted that all openings should be dimensioned from the centre of the opening to the outside edge of the corner post. Whilst the heights of the girts will be of more importance on the framing plan, the floor lines should be shown on all framing plans in another coloured ink, as they will be needed in fixing the heights of the horizontal studding under sills and at heads of door openings. Framing plans of the floors will show in careful detail all the floor joists and any trimming for openings, such as staircase wells, flues, chimney breasts, chutes, lifts or trap-doors. Partitions will also be shown on these plans with openings marked in dimensions and the distances between studs dimensioned from centre to centre. Where partitions are double for sliding doors and the studs placed flatways, a note should be made on the plan to that effect.

The framing of roofs will also be shown on a roof plan and upon each elevation ; and it is of assistance to the carpenter if the angles of all hips and rafters be marked on carefully.

In giving height dimensions it should be remembered that whilst the interior dimensions from floor to glass line of the windows, and from floor to ceiling and to tops of doors and windows, is of more interest to the owner of the house and to the designer, yet the man who has to form the skeleton of the house will require to know the lengths to which the studs must be cut and the heights at which the girts are to be fixed. Consequently more prominence should be given to these dimensions on framing plans than to the former which will predominate on the elevations and sections. However, the greatest care should be taken that these two sets of dimensions correspond and total the same. From which it will be seen that the figuring of dimensions is a much more important part of a framework building than is the case with a building of masonry or brickwork.

FIG. 10.—OLD HALF-TIMBERING.

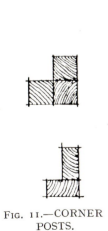

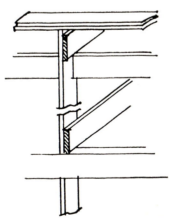

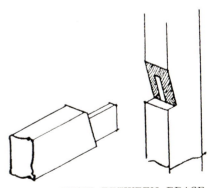

FIG. 11.—CORNER POSTS.

FIG. 12.—JOINT BETWEEN POST AND GIRT.

FIG. 13.—JOINT BETWEEN BRACE AND POST.

FLOORS IN FRAMEWORK

So far as the floors themselves and the joists are concerned, there is little difference in their construction in framework from that obtaining in solid masonry ; except in so far as an underfloor is always employed and the method of jointing the rafters to the plates, sills and girts is somewhat different.

The spacing of the floor joists will correspond to that of the studs, as they are fixed to the sides of the studs.

Joists on the ground floor are framed to the sills in the manner already described, and they may also be cut as shown in Fig. 14, when the plate is twice notched. However, as the feet of the common studs and posts are tenoned into mortises cut into the sills to prevent extra

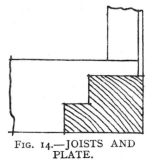

FIG. 14.—JOISTS AND PLATE.

cutting, the joists are often hung to the sills by means of cast-iron hangers, as shown in Fig. 15, which method has the additional advantage that whilst the sill does not require so much cutting, neither does the joist need weakening by the shoulders cut in its depth, but the whole depth of the square end of the joist is carried in the hanger.

In preparing framing plans for floors the position of all openings and partitions over and under must first be marked on in a different coloured ink. The dimensions should be figured from the outside of the outer walls and to the centre of all intermediate framings. When partitions come above a floor, but are not supported by partitions underneath, double floor joists or joists having cross pieces of joists run between them to form bridging at right angles must be inserted. Trimmers and trimming joists must be of greater strength as described earlier and common joists are usually laid at 16" from centre to centre. The method of fixing the ends of floor joists on outer walls in timber has already been

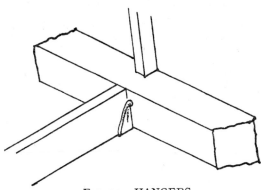

FIG. 15.—HANGERS.

described ; and so far as the internal partitions coming one over another, either of the following methods is employed. In the first, the lower partition is constructed complete with its head terminated under the floor joists, and on the top of the floor joists the sill of the upper partition is laid. In the second method the head of the lower partition is the sill of the upper. The former, however, is not recommended, as the floor joists shrink across the grain as much as $\frac{1}{2}"$ to the foot, with the result that the upper partition will drop and the plaster crack. More particularly would this be noticeable when the floor joists are supported by a beam and the sill of the partition is laid on the floor joists, as occurs in basements of the American type, when not only the depth of the floor joist, but also that of the beam has to be reckoned with in the shrinkage, and the consequent drop in the partition above will be over an inch, which is a serious matter.

The Basement

The origin of the basement is the saving of domestic work. The central hot air furnace or boiler therein renders possible the doing without fireplaces ; and everyone who has ever had anything to do with housework knows for how much of it fires are responsible. By the introduction of a central furnace or boiler the housewife is saved from all connection with any fire except the kitchen range, and that not the tremendous affair we are cursed with in England. The man of the house attends, and only twice daily, to the furnace. That the central furnace is responsible for a considerable amount of dust is acknowledged ; but this need not be so. With the system in vogue of open gratings to admit the heated air direct into the rooms, and with these gratings placed in the floors, also with the cold air intake from the outside on the ground level, a certain amount of dust is unavoidable. But it would be no difficult matter to place the gratings above the floor level, and to filter both the cold air at its intake and also the hot air at its exit in such a manner as would prevent most if not all dust. The dust, too, from a furnace mostly gathers in light fluffy balls, which may be easily swept up, and is not like the dust from coal-ash, which settles well into and upon everything inside the room.

Hot-air furnaces, it is true, have been in this country made somewhat upon the lines of those in use in Canada and the States ; but they were not readily taken up, though how far prejudice and how far the un-adaptability of brick and stone walls to the housing of air-ducts entered into this failure it would be difficult to say. But, as in the present instance the innovation is suggested only for temporary wooden houses, the latter objection does not apply. Another item which would militate against the use of the hot-air furnace in small quantities would be the initial cost of their manufacture ; but were these to be manufactured in sufficient numbers to supply the houses required, that feature would disappear.

However, the inclusion of a furnace or boiler in a cellar materially affects the design of the house, and that the result need not be unpleasing to the eye is a fact. The matter is merely one of proportion. We have grown used to our comfortable-looking cottages and houses which nestle upon the ground and are naturally prejudiced against buildings perched up in the air. Neither do we care for cellars of the wholly underground type. In Canada and America this difficulty is partially overcome by a compromise in which half the height of the cellar is built underground and the other half above the ground line.

But as in frame building the wood framework begins at the ground-floor level and the cellar walls are usually constructed of either brick, masonry or concrete, with a properly designed water table or string course running round at the line of junction between the sub-basement wall and the framing over, it is not impossible by any means to give the building an appearance of breadth, which is the chief characteristic of the English exterior that we like so much.

When sub-basements are formed in this manner the plates to the outer wall are bolted to the concrete basement wall and beams are run across the area resting on this plate for the support of the internal partitions. These beams are given additional support in their length by means of posts at distances of 10' 0" apart, resting on concrete foundation generally 6" wider each way than the post, and having wooden caps and bases. The caps are more serviceable when formed of wedges, in order that any shrinkage in the post can be taken up at any time by means of a tap or so on the wedges when required, which will tighten up the junction of the post with the beam. In the same way, if desired, the base may be tightened also.

The basement is usually divided into coal store, laundry and furnace or boiler-room, the two deciding features in this being that the water for the laundry should come under the water pipes above to save expense in unnecessary plumbing, and also that the furnace or boiler should come as near as may be to the centre of the building, which affords better heating and consequently effects a saving in fuel. All the partitions in the basement are usually formed of 2" by 6" studding, and those to the laundry and larder should be sheathed with matched boarding which may be painted. Though a better covering for all the partitions of a cellar is some form of asbestos sheeting, which is fireproof and can also be painted in the laundry and larder. Another point worthy of note in planning the basement is that the furnace door should face a direction which gives ample elbow room for the use of the stoking shovel and iron, and in that direction also the coal cellar should lie.

The furnace itself will rest upon a brick base, but the services of the carpenter will be required in forming a cold air duct on the floor to the bottom of the furnace. This duct is usually framed of boarding lined with zinc and connects to an opening in the outer wall facing the prevalent wind, but in districts which are exposed it is desirable to have a cold air supply from the opposite side of the building also. Each of these ducts should be provided with a damper, which is generally a square piece of wood made to slide up and down in guides on the inside of the duct and kept up when open by a pin. These two ducts are necessary to prevent strong winds sucking the air from the house and down the furnace, and so reversing the natural operation of the furnace.

The *Fresh Air* inlet in the outer wall should, if possible, be raised above the level of the ground to prevent the suction of dust ; and in any case it should be provided with a fine gauze screen on the sash which is fitted into the frame in the wall.

TRUSSED PARTITIONS.—Where partitions have any great span in frame buildings it is advisable that they should be trussed, more so than in masonry buildings. The additional cost is slight, and the sagging of the floors, due to the weight of the partition, can be prevented thereby.

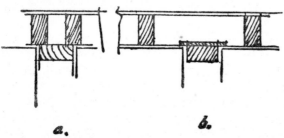

FIG. 16.—CROSS PARTITIONS—ALTERNATIVES.

A properly formed trussed partition may also serve to support the floor above when desired. The caps of partitions consist of 2″ by 4″ studs single or double nailed to the tops of the upright studs ; and when the partition is parallel to the floor joists cross pieces are inserted from joist to joist and the cap nailed to this. Boards about 3″ wider than the cap are spiked to the cap to give fixing for the lath ends.

The formation of *corners* in intersecting partitions is achieved in a variety of ways, as shown in Fig. 16, *a*, the object of all being the same, viz. to allow of a fixing on each face for the ends of the laths. Another method is shown in Fig. 16, *b* ; of these the former is perhaps the best of any, as it gives a stronger angle and allows a better fixing for the laths.

For the prevention of the transmission of sound from one room to another the studs in a partition are staggered as shown in Fig. 17. This is practically the same thing as building two separate partitions so far as the uprights are concerned, but being interspaced they interlace with one another, and so take up less space. One sill and one head serve for both sets of studding, but they require to be out of 2″ by 6″.

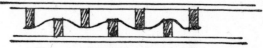

FIG. 17.—SOUND DEADENING.

For additional sound prevention the space between the two sets of uprights is filled with slag wood or sound proofing paper nailed to the inner faces of the studs.

CHIMNEY BREASTS AND FLUES

In framework outer walls chimney breasts and flues are built in bricks or concrete as in buildings having masonry walls, but with the difference that the breasts are not carried up to the full height of the room in which the fireplace occurs. The desire being to save brickwork, the breasts are arched over and contracted to the flue size as soon as is possible. If there are other flues from below these are formed into a stack with the one in question, and serve as base for the fireplace above, such corbelling out being done as is necessary to carry any chimney breast there may be above. But in order to give the appearance of a chimney breast in the room vertical studding is carried up from the point at which the brickwork begins to set back. A 2″ by 4″ plate is rested on the last flush brick course, and from this short lengths of 2″ by 4″ studding are run up to a head piece under the floor or ceiling joists. Where sufficient space cannot be obtained for the 4″ by 2″ studs to be set on the chimney front in the usual manner, they are set sideways with their narrow width from back to front ; and failing space for this, the brickwork is battened with 1″ battens vertically.

Where central heating is adopted rooms are frequently built without fireplaces, and any flue which passes through them, as that from the furnace and kitchen, is built of brickwork, and should have its face battened or framed in with vertical studding. This last is perhaps the best method, as the studding can be framed in such a manner so that it does not touch the brickwork, and so offers less opportunity to fire arising from the over-heating of any woodwork touching the brickwork, though where flues are lined with fireclay linings, as they are usually in American frame buildings, this risk is not so great.

WALLS : SHEATHING.—As soon as the first story is erected, or in the balloon frame as soon as the studding is secured to the plate and joists, the studs are covered with rough boarding. Hemlock, spruce and Western White pine are most frequently used for this purpose on account of cheapness. In the Western States redwood and Oregon pine being local are preferred for the same reason. It is advisable to fix this boarding diagonally to serve as additional wind brace, and in the best work it is planed on the inner face. The openings for doors and windows may be cut out after the sheathing is nailed.

ROOFS.—In sheathing roofs rough boarding as last described is used laid close at right angles to the rafters. But when this practice is adopted there should be also roofing battens nailed on to its upper surface, to allow of an air space coming between the boarding and roof covering. A cheaper method, saving the battens, is to lay the rough boarding with a space of 2″ between each board, but where the roof space is used for rooms such a method is not recommended, as it provides little protection against driving snow or rain. A waterproof building paper when used is the best protection against this, and a point rarely observed is that it should be placed *over* instead of under the battens.

POSSIBLE TREATMENTS FOR FRAME BUILDINGS IN ENGLAND.—Whilst the original frame building was a half-timbered one, and though in the country of its rebirth the proper half-timbering was dropped, yet frame building having proved adequate in climates far more extreme than ours, there would seem no reason why it should not be reintroduced in its

FIG. 18.—COTTAGES AT BALCOMBE, SUSSEX. Modern half-timbering by H. Bryant Newbold, F.R.I.B.A.

modified form into this country. Also, even if there are objections for climatic reasons unknown to the author against the use of framework covered with shingles or siding, these, whatever they may be, should not prevent its use when covered with other materials of a more permanent nature.

ASBESTOS sheeting prepared in 4′ 0″ and 6′ 0″ lengths proves a very satisfactory covering, and when butt jointed and the joints covered with 2″ strips provided for that purpose by the manufacturers is watertight and fireproof. Asbestos sheeting can be cut with the saw and bored with a brace and bit or bradawl. The method of fixing is to nail to the studs through holes bored as stated by means of special flat-headed galvanised nails also provided. All openings should be trimmed round with the specially made strips and bored and nailed similarly. This sheeting may be obtained in grey or red, but it is perhaps doubtful if the weather will have much effect upon its tone such as is admired so much in the case of brickwork. However, the resultant building for one of a temporary nature is of sufficient durability to meet what is required of it, and roofed with asbestos roofing in the manner described in another place it is cool in summer, warm in winter and should be as fireproof as most.

EXPANDED METAL AND ROUGH CASTING.—Great strides have been made of recent years in reinforced concrete, and whilst rough cast spread over expanded metal may not be regarded as coming within the meaning of the term, it is difficult to see what else it is when properly prepared. Reinforced concrete is a preparation of gravel or stone, sand and cement having steel embedded within it. This is the case with expanded metal. For cheaper work loose netting of small mesh is nailed to a wooden framework and has cement plaster finished rough cast well pressed through the interstices. The method usually adopted by the author in covering frame-built houses in Canada is to nail the expanded metal lathing to the studs, the strips being laid horizontally. However, as with poor sand or cement and unseasoned timber there was danger of cracks appearing on the studding lines, narrow battens were introduced across the studs and the expanded metal fixed thereto vertically. If the mixture of the plaster and rough cast has been correct, the result is a thin strip of reinforced concrete strong enough to resist any vagaries of the weather except earthquakes, which no form of building construction has as yet been discovered to withstand. Further, it is not necessary to go far in research into reinforced concrete to be made aware that walls built in that material do not rely upon their thickness for their impermeability. As this outer covering does not support any of the weight of the building, it would be difficult to see how a more damp-proof form of construction could be devised. To make additionally sure in this last respect, one of the several methods of waterproofing cement work might be added.

ROOFS may also be constructed in this way, the objection to their flat and uninteresting surface being overcome in either of the following ways. The first consists simply in running a trowel along a straight edge and so form straight or wavy lines in the outer cement cover before it is set. In the second the surface is moulded by means of boards grooved as shown being pressed down upon the cement before setting and afterwards removed when set. Over the rafters rough boarding is nailed, and on to these battens at not more than 2′ 0″ are fixed horizontally. Over these the expanded metal is laid, and on to this the cement is pressed with a plasterer's trowel. Where waterproof building paper is used, its most serviceable position is under the rough boarding and over the rafters. The ridges used are half-round cast cement channels, which also serve for hips.

WEATHER BOARDING.—The durability of weather boarding has been sufficiently proved of old times, and also by its recent revival, for anything further to need saying in its support. It is especially suited for use with frame work, the most satisfactory form of construction being always that in which there is homogeneity. Wood against wood makes a good binding construction, but of course cannot be absolved from the danger of fire.

Weather boarding is sawn to any size required, but is usually from a 10″ plank sawn diagonally across its thickness to form two weather boards. To ensure proper fixing, and at the same time additional air space, battens may be nailed horizontally to the studding for the weather boarding to be nailed to, and if this be started from the bottom and fixed working upward, the nailings of each board will be covered by the board above it, which will prevent rusting. It is a point worthy of note here that in oak used for weather boards, or for any other outside work, galvanised nails should be used to prevent rust marks running down the face of the woodwork. Cross-cut planks, especially of elm, are used for weather boarding. These are of irregular sizes, and have a wavy edge of the natural shape of the outside of the tree.

There are a variety of ways of forming angles in weather boarding on framework buildings, some of which are shown in Figs. 24 and 25. In one an additional strip is fixed to the chamfered corner of the corner stud and against this the weather boarding is butted. In another method, consisting of a board placed angularly fixed to the inner stud, is shown, but this method necessitates additional labour in cutting the ends of the weather boards with splays. In a third method a separate cover board is fixed over the weather boarding and nailed through to the stud; which is perhaps the most weatherproof of all the methods used. A method is practised but has very little to commend it save possibly a certain rusticity of effect. It consists simply in the weather boarding of one side being produced from 3″ to 4″ beyond the face of the other side and the ends of the other weather boarding being butted against this projection. But the method can hardly be described as weathertight, whatever else it may be.

WEATHERINGS.—Frame buildings being usually constructed on some form of solid foundation wall require a weathering or slope outwards at the bottom of the weather boarding to throw off the rainwater from the joint between the two materials. Three methods of effecting this are shown in Figs. 4, 5 and 6. Fig. 4 shows the plate produced beyond the face of the stud and masonry wall under, and having a chamfered edge to take the bottom course of weather boarding; Fig. 5, a tilter bracket cut in under the bottom weather board; and Fig. 6, a water table, consisting of two boards framed at right angles, nailed to fixing blocks built in the foundation wall.

OPENINGS IN WEATHER BOARDING.—The weather boarding round openings for doors and windows should have cover boards fixed at right angles to the frames of the openings produced, to cover the ends of the weather boards and to be nailed thereto.

SHINGLES.—For roofing in wood thin, flat, tapering strips from $\frac{5}{16}$" to $\frac{1}{2}$" at the butt in thickness, in widths varying from $2\frac{1}{2}$" to 14" and usually 18" long, are used as a covering. They are put up in bundles four to the thousand, a thousand common shingles meaning the equivalent of 1,000 shingles 4" wide.

The most common wood for shingles is cedar, but the best and most durable are those made from cypress and redwood. Cedar is much cheaper than cypress or redwood, but redwood has slower burning qualities. The old-fashioned split pine shingles were very durable, but the shingles now used are practically all sawn.

It is perhaps on account of their inflammability that shingles are not used in this country, except for church spires, where lightness is particularly desirable. Neither are shingles so durable as slates or tiles; but against these disadvantages may be offset the advantage of their lightness, rendering possible much tighter construction in the roof timbers. Also methods of treatment have been devised rendering them less inflammable; and experience proves that the majority of fires in buildings do not start from the roof downwards, but from some inflammable material within the building, and that if a building is once well afire the roof timbers will burn whether roofed with slates or tiles or other incombustible material. A great feature in their favour is that shingles may be stained to any colour desired, rendering possible, particularly when the walls are also sheeted with hanging shingle, colour schemes of very pleasing appearance.

Patterns are frequently introduced into the laying of shingles, when equal widths are bunched together, being termed "dimensioned." These vary from 4" to 6" widths. Also for the purpose of presenting decorative patterns when laid or hung, shingles are prepared with sawn butts. The best quality shingles should be free from sap, shakes and knots, the Washington and Oregon cedar being the most free from these defects. Sound knots are permissible in pine and cypress when not closer than 8" to the butt.

Shingles are graded into qualities and marked, but as the grade marks vary for different woods and localities, the safest specification will be "best quality," which are generally marked "extra" or "prime."

LAYING.—Shingles are laid from the eaves upwards to a line or straight edge. The lowest course should be laid double or triple, the other course being single, unless, as is often desired, for the obtaining of a more broken surface, every so often a double course is introduced. Each shingle should be secured by two "3 penny" nails driven 8" up from the butt, and in the best work galvanised nails are used.

DURABILITY.—There are still standing in the Southern States houses built of shingles over 100 years ago, and in good preservation to-day. It may be reasonably claimed for redwood and cypress shingles that if dipped in oil or creosote twenty-five years will be their average durability. Redwood is, however, more durable than cedar, and should last up to fifty years.

In laying, the courses should lap so that not more than one-third of the length will appear. 16″ shingles should not be laid to show more than $4\frac{1}{2}$″, and 18″ shingles not more than $5\frac{1}{2}$″.

In supervision it is well to see that each shingle is properly nailed. The exposure to the weather should also be checked, as the greater this is the less shingle will be required to cover the area, and a saving to the contractor results.

QUANTITIES.—The following table will serve as a guide to the number of shingles of average widths required to cover various areas when laid with different exposure.

TABLE SHOWING AREA COVERED BY 1,000 SHINGLES

Laid to show.	sq. ft.	Number to a square.
$4\frac{1}{4}$″	118	847
$4\frac{1}{2}$″	125	800
$4\frac{3}{4}$″	131	758
5″	138	720
$5\frac{1}{2}$″	152	655
6″	166	600

PAPER LINING.—As with tiles and slates a layer of good stout waterproof building paper should be laid under the shingles, though where the shingles are laid upon close boarding, unless they are dipped in preservative, the paper is apt to cause rotting. Battens over the boarding laid to a proper gauge to take the nails will prevent this, and the paper should then be laid under the battens and over the boarding. Asbestos felting will serve the same purpose, also being a preventive against fire, and will keep the building cool in summer and warm in winter.

FIG. 19.—RIDGING TO SHINGLE ROOF.

HIPS AND RIDGES.—The top course is laid with shortened shingles, when the ridge may be formed in any of the following ways:

Special made equal-thicknessed shingles are laid on over the top course meeting at the ridge, a start being made on each ridge at each end, the ridge shingles laid in opposite directions meeting at the centre of the ridge. Over this meeting-point a single equal-thicknessed shingle is laid on both slopes to cover the joint of ridge shingles, as shown in Fig. 19.

Alternatively, the top course being cut to fit, saddle boards 5″ by 7″, rebated at the angle of the pitch of the roof, are nailed on to the ridge.

A third method is to fix over a ridge roll an ornamental galvanised iron cresting, or an ornamental wood cresting may be constructed out of a plank on edge fixed to the ridge.

FIG. 20.—RIDGE.

HIPS may be formed in a manner similar to the second method described for ridging. Or shingles of a width equal to a shingle and a half are cut to the slant of the hip, and have a wood cover mould bevelled out in its underside nailed on throughout the length of the hip to conceal the joist.

On church spires the hips are formed by a $1\frac{1}{4}$″ wood bead nailed to the boarding on the line of the hip, and covered with long strips of zinc, copper or lead 10″ wide, turned over the bead, and spread out over the shingles, the edges of the shingles being lapped over the flashing, and laid close to the bead.

FIG. 21.— TRIMMED SHINGLE.

Trimmed shingles are used to form a close-fitting hip of the shape shown in Fig. 21. Over each pair of hip shingles a piece of zinc, 5″ by 5″, bent to the proper angle, is nailed to fit, so that it comes just above the bottom of the next shingle. The edges of the hip shingles are lapped alternately, with the result that a weathertight joint of neat appearance is made.

In the first method mentioned the shingles are similarly lapped alternately, being square-shaped 4″ wide.

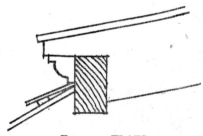

FIG. 22.—FLATS.

FLATS IN SHINGLE ROOFS.—Where flats occur in shingle roofs, they are terminated over a wood or metal moulding, as shown in Fig. 22, or alternatively a flat or chamfered fillet may be used. The lead or zinc covering to the flat is turned up under the fillet or moulding, and between the moulding a trimmer. The moulding being screwed to the trimmer holds the lead in position and makes a watertight joint.

In Mansard roofs the upper slope is treated as above, having a 3″ deal in addition laid along the top course of shingles to the lower slope, as shown in Fig. 23.

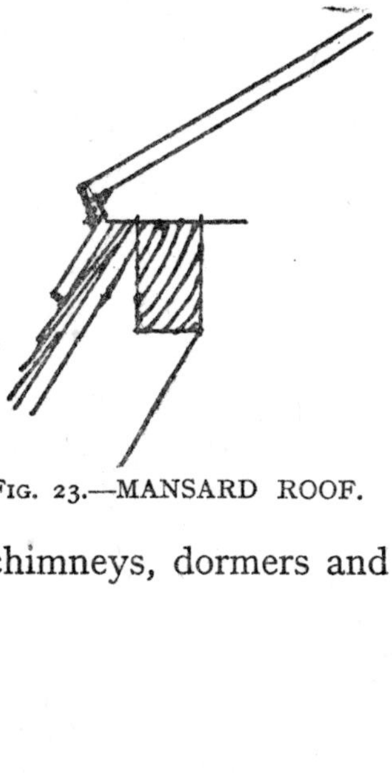

FIG. 23.—MANSARD ROOF.

FLASHINGS.—Where roofs are pierced by chimneys, dormers and skylights metal flashings are used to prevent leakage of water through the joint.   This metal in the Eastern States is zinc, but in California copper being cheaper is much used.   Where the opening is caused by a chimney of brickwork or masonry, or where sloping roofs abut against masonry walls, the flashings are strips of metal 7″ wide, which are laid over one shingle and under the next above.   Each flashing projects for a third of its length over the flashing below it.

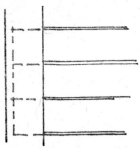

FIG. 24.—CORNER BOARDS

About 3″ of the flashing is turned up against the brickwork, and over this, let into the joints in the masonry and cemented, is a counter flashing. The counter flashing when in lead is wedged with strips of lead rolled into a wedge shape before the cement is pointed in.   At the lower end of a chimney, on the face which runs at right angles to the slope of the roof, a metal apron is laid on the shingles and turned up against the chimney and into the joint.   In this case the cover flashing may be dispensed with, though a better finish results from its introduction here also.   Above the chimney a small pent roof, known in America as a " cricket," is formed in wood and covered with metal.   This form is employed where the snowfall is great, as it is serviceable in preventing a lodgment.   The metal should be turned up against the top vertical face of the chimney and counter flashed, and also 4″ depth main roof under the shingles. Alternatively to this last, where the snowfall is not liable to be so great, a simple wood gutter having a slope one way is covered with metal dressed as already described and turned up under the shingles.   This gutter is formed by nailing a short length of rafter to the side of the common rafters and butted against the trimmer, over which boarding 9″ wide is laid and the metal dressed over as before described.   In better workmanship another 9″ board is laid along the rafters up the slope of the roof, having at its upper edge a tilting fillet fixed.   This last provides additional fixing for the metal covering and serves to throw up the bottom rows of shingles.

In snow districts it is important to see that the flashing is carried up to a greater height than elsewhere, so that the water collecting from snow melting on the roof shall not rise above it.

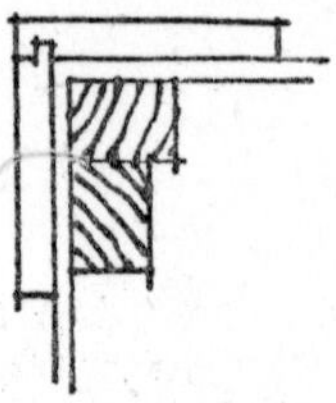

Covering of Wooden Walls

FIG. 25.—CORNER BOARDS.

SHINGLES.—Shingles are also used for covering frame walls.   These are hung in such a manner that three thicknesses of shingle cover the wall at all points.   They are similar to those used on roofs, with the exception that the butts are deeper and also ornamental-shaped butts for patterned work are more often introduced.   Random-length shingles are sometimes used, but the result is a somewhat untidy one.   Wall shingles should not be wider than 8″ nor narrower than 3½″, and they are hung with from 5″ to 6″ to the weather.

The corners of buildings hung with shingle may be lapped alternately as explained for roofs, or angle boards may be superimposed as shown in Figs. 28 and 29. These boards are usually 4″ to 5″ wide, and similar boards 2″ or 3″ wide, with the angle the opposite way, are inserted in internal angles.

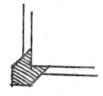

At door and window openings the joint should be flushed with lead or zinc, building paper only being substituted in cheaper work. A 5″ to 6″ board is also used to cover the joint between the window and the shingle.

WATER TABLES.—Where shingles come down upon a masonry sub-wall, a tilting fillet is inserted under the bottom course of shingles, which should be a double or treble course. Where

FIG. 26.   FIG. 27.

FIGS. 28 AND 29.

a decided tilt is desired, a water table of the gallons bracket type is introduced.

CLAPBOARDING.—The clapboards as used in the New England States are 4′ 0″ long by 6″ wide, ½″ thick at the butt, and ⅞″ at the top edge. It corresponds to our weather-boarding. In the Western States a combined clapboard is used, being about 12″ wide and having the appearance from outside of being composed of three clapboards fixed together, as shown in Fig. 28.

Clapboards are cut by circular saw from the circumference to the centre of the log, the log being revolved after each cut, with the result that every board being quarter sawn there is very little shrinkage or warpage.

In fixing clapboards they are laid from the top

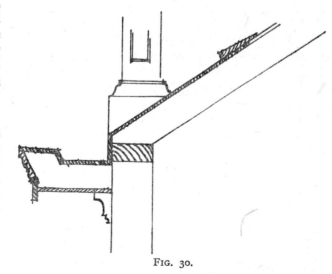

FIG. 30.

downwards, and care should be taken to see that they are butted at the angles against a splayed or square angle board as shown in Fig. 28. The best clapboards are white pine and should be free from loose knots or sap.

SIDING is another name for composite clapboarding, as already described, and is also rebated at its bottom edge and moulded on its outer

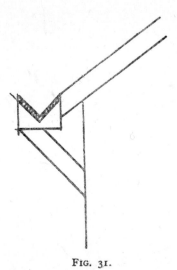

face to various designs. The ends should come over a stud, and be double nailed and butted with white lead and oil. Another name for composite clapboarding is drop siding. The rebating effects a saving in nails ; also this method of nailing prevents cracking in the event of shrinkage occurring. The most durable woods for this type of clapboarding are cypress and redwood, and next to these soft pine, the harder pines being too brittle and likely to split when being nailed.

Though clapboarding is nailed directly to the studs, the practice is not a good one ; an under-covering of unwrought boarding should be introduced over the studs, preferably fixed diagonally when it acts as a brace to the studding.

EAVES GUTTERS IN SHINGLE ROOFS.— Eaves gutters to shingle slopes may be either fixed at the feet of the rafters, as to tile roofs, in which case they may be moulded or half-round metal gutters or square or V-shaped wooden gutters, or where the snowfall is great they may be found as shown in Fig. 32, where the gutter is formed in line with the vertical face of the wall under and the roof continued below it carried on " lookouts." When this form is used it enables narrow shingles to be carried over the gutter every other shingle, by which provision the snow is prevented from blocking the gutter.

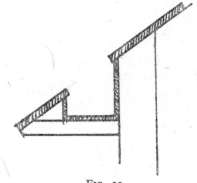

FIG. 32.

Wooden gutters at the feet of the rafters are either boxed up out of flat boards to form a three-sided square, or they may be hollowed out of the solid, being rounded inside and square outside, or two boards are formed into a V-shape, as shown in Fig. 31, and strutted up from the wall face.

FIG. 33.

WOODEN DOWNSPOUTS.—Wooden downspouts are formed of two semi-cylinders about $\frac{5}{8}''$ thick, grooved and spliced at their edges. When formed of cypress they are the most durable. The swan necks are moulded in two parts, and are finished at the top by a wooden moulding turned in two parts and nailed to the pipes.

Wooden downspouts are also boxed square, in which case the angles should be rebated and bound with copper strips. The swan neck at the top in this case becomes a splayed angle and the offset at the bottom is of the same form.

Whilst reasonably durable under ordinary conditions, wooden gutters have the failing that if allowed to become choked frost will split them, owing to the sudden expansion of the water inside on turning to ice, though perhaps this may hardly be regarded as a failing of the downspout, as they are easily kept free if cleaned out periodically.

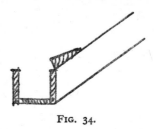

FIG. 34.

EAVES CONSTRUCTION.—It is perhaps a peculiar coincidence that in many of the parts where wooden construction is used externally for build-

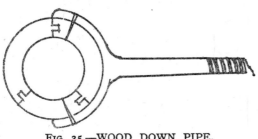

FIG. 35.—WOOD DOWN PIPE.

ings the weather is more extreme than it is with us where brick and masonry are customary. Whatever may be the reason underlying this, it is obvious that to cope with such extremes the fashioning of the eaves becomes a matter of first importance. When it is a question of snow, it will be readily recognised that the water which collects from melting is a more serious

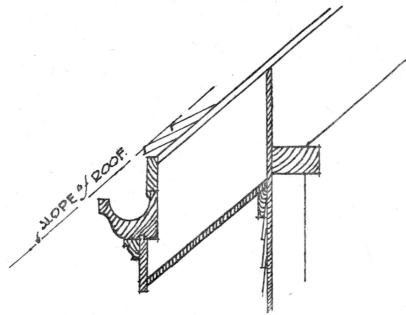

FIG. 36.

matter than that which falls as rain, owing to the fact that the snow lies upon the roof and on melting gives rise to a far greater volume of

water than could find lodgment when falling as rain. In the latter
event, it will be conducted away as it falls.

Also in countries where the rainfall is excessive and of a semi-tropical

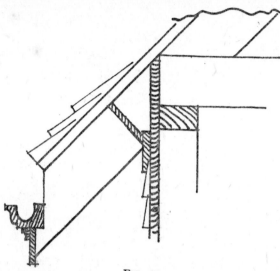

downpour in its nature, the
projection of the eaves from
the face of the building will
be equally as important as
where considerable shade is
desirable from the excessive
heat of the sun.

From this it will be
gathered that the construction
of the eaves is an important
matter in wooden buildings,
and that in a country spreading over such a large area and
having such varied climates
as North America the methods
employed will vary considerably.

In the snow districts of
the east and north a flatter

FIG. 37.

pitch at the eaves is necessary to prevent the snow sliding when a thaw
sets in. Also a wide gutter and a snow rail will be required. In Northern
States the gutters are often kept below the level of the roof, with the inten-

tion that the
snow should be
facilitated in fall-
ing, but snow
rails are prefer-
able. These con-
sist of either
wood or metal
railings 12" to 18"
high, run along
the roof 2'0" back
from the eaves,
resting on a 2" by
6" plate, in which
holes are bored
to allow the rain-
water passage.

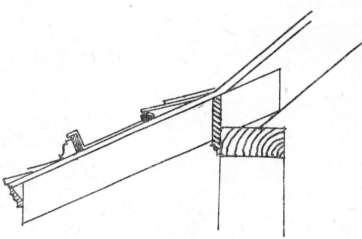

FIG. 38.

In the latter case, where it is desired to give the snow a chute, the
gutter is cut from the solid out of 5" by 7" stuff, having a 1⅛" fascia
rebated on to its top edge, and a cover mould beneath with a lower fascia
tenoned into its bottom edge. The rafter foot is cut to take the

gutter and upper fascia as shown, and the gutter is nailed to each rafter as shown. An alternative method is next shown in Fig. 37, where the upper fascia rests against the wall face and the underside of the roof boarding. The gutter is then rested on the notched rafter in the same manner as before, having a cover mould and under fascia only. The shingles are tilted upwards in their bottom course in the first case by the projection of the upper fascia, and in the second by a feather-edged tilting fillet nailed on to the roof boarding under the bottom course. The upper fascia, especially when fixed as last described, serves the additional purpose of excluding draughts in very windy districts from any rooms there may be in the roof. In specially exposed positions these fascia sections should be grooved into the rafters to make the joint addition- ally weather-proof.

Where it is desired to give the eaves a less pitch than that of the rafters, the rafters may be cut off at the outer edge of the wall-plate and false rafters nailed on to their sides. In this case, to avoid too great a leverage, the gutter is sometimes formed on the upper surface of the roof by means of a 3″ by 1″ strip nailed through the shingles to the roof boarding or rafters and having knees supporting it on its lower side.

An adaptation of the method last described to that used in conjunction with the cut rafters as previously detailed is shown in Fig. 41, where the gutter consists of two boards nailed together at right angles, the

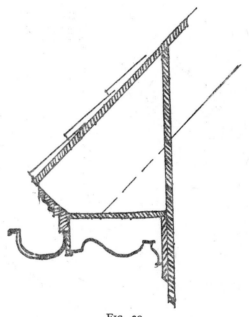

FIG. 39.

lower or bottom one being 10″ wide and the upright one being 4″. The 4″ board is fixed at such a position as will enable its top edge to come just below the line of the shingles if produced, and sufficiently far up the lower board to allow of a 2″ bracket or knee being nailed in for its support. The notch cut from the upper surface of the rafter feet is 2″ deep measured at right angles, but has a vertical top face to cut in under the roof boarding which is projected 1″ beyond this upright face. An upper fascia is fixed between the wall face and the underside of the board and cut in between the rafter feet as before described ; and where additional finish is desired a cover mould may be run along under the rafters at their point of junction with the face of the outer wall.

WOODEN CORNICES ON WOODEN BUILDINGS.—The wooden gutter is sometimes replaced by a metal one, and the roof terminated by means

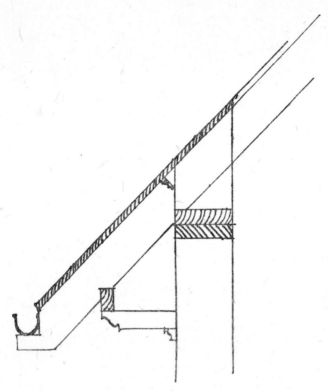

FIG. 40.—OPEN CORNICE.

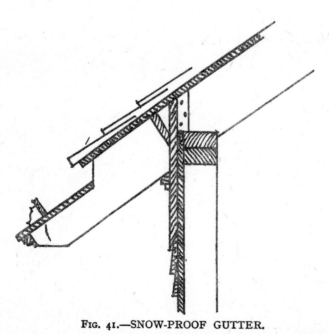

FIG. 41.—SNOW-PROOF GUTTER.

of a cornice constructed in wood. A typical method of this is shown in Fig. 39, where the rafter feet are projected beyond the wall face about 12″, and have a horizontal board fixed to their ends and to the boarding of the wall face. On the lower face of this horizontal board matched lining is nailed to form a soffit. To the outer ends of the rafter feet cut splayed is fixed a moulded fascia having a vertical batten as its lower member; and against the wall is fixed a secondary fascia. Where desired, brackets are nailed to the underside of the fascia and the wall face. These may be moulded, carved or plain.

More elaborate cornices having a balustrading above are met with, especially in the Southern States. In these the top member of the cornice becomes the gutter. The whole construction is put on after the roof is formed and, as a rule, has no actual constructive relationship with the rest of the building, except in so far as it carries the rainwater gutter. The mouldings of the cornice, and also the gutter, are nailed to framing having a horizontal member known as a " lookout " fixed at every 2' 0", spiked to the sides of the studding of the outer wall. The details of typical construction are shown in Fig. 30, the essential point being that a drip should be formed as at the point A by means of a horizontal member in the projecting part of the cornice, to prevent rainwater running down the face of the cornice. The gutter is framed in behind the top member, or, as is frequently the case, it is of metal, and then becomes the top member, and is bracketed to the lookouts with metal brackets. Above the gutter comes the balustrade, concerning which it is important that the feet of the posts should be covered with tin, zinc or lead to prevent rotting. Also the bottom rail of the balustrading should be kept up 2" above the roof. But where snow is to be expected, it is wiser to form the gutter behind the balustrading where it will be apt to collect. This, of course, applies only where the roof is a sloping one behind the balustrading. And, incidentally, it may be mentioned, though often met with in this position, it is not clear that a balustrading has any logical reason for its existence. The reason for a balustrading is to serve as a safeguard round the edges of a flat upon which persons may walk, but with a sloping roof this purpose no longer exists. On the other hand, where balustradings bound flats they will generally be formed on coping walls, at the base of which the gutter will be framed in the manner customary against any other vertical wall, and have out-falls therefrom cut through the opening wall to weep out over the gutter in the cornice.

OPEN WOODEN CORNICES in which the rafter ends are exposed have a more logical basis for their employment. Such a one is shown in Fig. 40, where a moulded bracket or " lookout " carries an additional plate supporting the rafter feet, into which it is notched as shown. The ends of the rafter feet are sometimes shaped and sometimes splay cut, and to these the gutter is screwed. For the purpose of giving a heavier appearance the rafter feet are thickened out, becoming 2" by 12", and in their upper angle and under the roof boarding, which must now be wrought, is fixed a cover mould as shown. The enlarged rafter feet are usually made of white pine prepared for painting, and in some cases these may be covered on their upper surface with white pine ceiling wrought side down with the roof boarding continued above it.

Gutters in open cornices look somewhat heavy when fixed at the ends of the rafters. Consequently, the method already described of inserting the gutter in a line with the face of the wall is resorted to.

CHAPTER III

JOINERY—INTRODUCTORY AND WINDOWS

Joinery Defined—Finish—Craftsmanship—Design—Processes—Joints: End-on—Square Cut Angle Joints—Mitre Cut Angle Joints—Solid or Boxed?—Bars or No Bars?—Proportion in Design—Types: Casement, Sash—Construction of the Sash—Construction of the Solid Frame —Shutters—Sliding Shutters—Double Sash—Bay-windows—Design.

JOINERY may be defined as being the woodwork finish, added either for practical use or decorative effect for the additional comfort of the occupant, rather than that woodwork essential to the support of the structure itself. All types of fitments and finishings come within the province of the joiner. Consequently, those being largely applied to the surface and visible when the building is complete, it will be obvious that greater accuracy of workmanship will be necessary. Processes and jointing will need to be executed with great precision and the details will be of a finer nature, more intricate and smaller in section.

FINISH

Whereas the carpenter's work is left with a sawn finish or trimmed with the adze, in joinery the surfaces and the joints are planed and trued with appropriate planes. Though sandpaper is frequently used to correct and cover up defects in inferior workmanship, skilled accuracy with the tools will render this unnecessary. The use of sandpaper can always be detected, and is objectionable, owing to the rounded finish which it gives to edges which should be square. At the same time, though the use of sandpaper is objectionable in the construction of joinery for the smoothing of surfaces to be painted, glasspapering, especially if an enamelled finish is desired, may be necessary.

CRAFTSMANSHIP

The skill required in hand-made joinery may be described as perhaps the highest of any used in the construction of a building. And owing to the speed required in modern times and the increasing cost of labour, the old-fashioned craftsman, to whom excellence of workmanship was the main inspiration, is fast disappearing, now to be met with rarely, save in country districts, backwaters of life remote from the rush of events. The fact is perhaps regrettable, but it is to be recognised ; and to the end that greater speed may be achieved hand-made work is fast being superseded by the use of machinery for all classes of joinery. Hand-made joinery will always be easily distinguished from machine-made, on account of its individual character ; but machines may be obtained to-day which will prepare woodwork for fitting together in every detail required. And where much duplication is required, the saving in time effected will be obvious. The fitting itself, however, still remains a hand process in most of the forms required in a building.

It is claimed for machine-made work that it is more accurate, and that machine-made joints are stronger than hand-made ; and whilst the former is no doubt true, the latter may be doubted. In any case, if the hand work is good this should not be so.

DESIGN

The work of the designer of joinery is even of more importance than in other trades. He must bear in mind that he is restricted to the use of small timbers, and he must design his joints so as to counteract any tendency to shift. At the same time his design must be economical of wood and construction. It has to be said that to design joinery a man must have worked at the bench ; and given subsequently the training necessary in draughtsmanship the most skilful designer is to be obtained.

However skilled the designer and craftsman may be, their efforts will be wasted unless thoroughly seasoned timber is supplied. Unseasoned timber will shift upon the slightest change in the humidity of the air and stopping by plugging with wood pegs or putty will at once be evident, and a sure sign of either poor workmanship or unseasoned wood.

As has been said, the designer of joinery must confine his work to the use of small surfaces, but in panelling this is hardly possible. Consequently, as of recent times it has become recognised as almost impossible to obtain wood sufficiently well seasoned for use in the large surfaces found in old work, ply-wood of from three to five thicknesses is becoming more generally used for surfaces and panels.

Also, owing to the increasing cost of the more valuable woods, a thin strip of the wood desired for the surface is superimposed on a cheaper woodwork ; and the practice once felt to be dishonest is becoming accepted as its use becomes more general.

PROCESSES

BEADING.—There are a variety of beads used in joinery, all consisting of rounded strips worked on the edge, corner or surface. *Quirked* beads have a sinking or groove on one side, and are rounded on the other ; whilst a *double-quirked* bead has a sinking on both sides. When double-quirked beads are worked on the corner, they are termed *staff, angle* or *return* beads. *Cocked* beads are raised from the surface ; and several beads running parallel and worked side by side are called *reeding*.

The reason for the sinking or groove is generally to cast a shadow over a joint to prevent the joint from being so obvious when the boards may pull apart.

BLOCKING.—When triangular and square blocks of wood are glued on the inner side of a joint between two boards, as in the underside of tread and rises of stairs, the practice is termed blocking.

BENDING.—The simplest method of bending wood is to cut slits or *kerfs* on the surface of the wood which will form the outerside of the curve. The cuts should be made to a depth not exceeding $\frac{1}{16}''$ from the face. If, however, it is desired to show the convex face of the woodwork, the cuts are made wedged shaped, then glued and the board bent backwards till the cuts are neatly joined. To give a smooth-finished concave face broader wedge-shape cuts are made, and fillets cut to fit glued in, the broader, outer surface, being rounded or otherwise treated.

CHAMFERING is the term given to the operation of planing off the angle of a board at 45°. A *stopped chamfer* is one which does not continue to the end of the board, as is often seen in the rails, mountings and styles of panelled doors.

GLUING.—Glue which is made from skin, horn and hoofs is in constant use in the joiners' shop, and consequently, as it must be used as hot as possible, the glue pot is kept on a permanent fire or burner. Plain joints as required in the surfaces of large panels are *shot*, i.e. very accurately planed with a square butt joint, warmed, both edges having been glued are clamped in the vice. When set the surplus glue which has squeezed out may be removed.

In grooved joints the glue is poured into the groove, and the boards treated in the same manner.

A practice growing much in use, especially in the ground work for veneered doors, is the joining of thin strips together with glue, to form a core over which the veneer in wide strips is afterwards glued.

PLANING.—In the joiners' shops the sawn balk timber, after having been sawn, is run through a machine which removes the rough sawn surface on one edge and one face. The timber is then turned over and run through the machine again, when the two remaining surfaces are smoothed or planed. This operation is termed *surfacing*. The timber is next run through a planing machine which can be adjusted to *plane* it to any required size. Hand planing of the surface is performed in the first or rough stage by a long plane known as a jack plane, and then smoothed by a shorter plane having less projection on the blade.

Special planes, described under "Joiners' Tools," are used for curved and moulded surfaces.

PLOUGHING.—Grooves cut with the grain are called plough grooves.

SAWING.—The operation of sawing is the rending and wearing away in sawdust of wood, either with or across the grain, by means of a toothed implement having the teeth twisted slightly outwards to right and left alternately to assist in the rending as the saw is worked either up and down by hand, or in one direction, as in the case of the machine circular saw. *Rip saws* are used with the grain, having larger and more widely twisted teeth ; whilst *hand* saws having smaller teeth are used across the grain. *Cross-cut* saws have a handle at each end, being worked by two men, as in saw-mills and in felling trees. Of the finer saws *tenon and dovetail* saws are made to cut across the grain, and their backs are stiffened by brass clamps being generally used flat, and not required to penetrate for the whole of their width.

Small tapering saws, used for cutting curves, are known as *compass* and *keyhole* saws.

As will be found more fully described under machinery, machine saws are either circular or *band* saws. *Circular* saws vary from a few inches to several feet in diameter. The cut is performed by that part of the edge travelling downwards, the wood being pushed forward to meet the saw. The *band* saw is formed of a continuous belt of steel with teeth on one edge and running over pulley wheels.

SCRIBING is the cutting out in profile the end or surface of one moulded or irregular piece of wood to fit over the irregular surface of another, as in the case of mouldings meeting at an angle. For example, skirtings are scribed instead of being mitred, when the end of one skirting board has the moulding of the other cut in it in reverse. But this method is not applicable where any of the mouldings are under cut. Skirtings which are cut to fit a narrow space, but to line at the top with deeper skirtings, are also said to be *scribed* over or round that which prevents their being of the same width as the general run of the skirting with which they are desired to line.

SHOOTING.—The edges of boards when planed square are said to be shot.

SPLAYING is chamfering at any angle other than 45°.

STOPPING.—Any moulding chamfer or bead which is either splayed at the end or butted into a square shoulder, and does not continue to the end of the member, is said to be stopped. Rails of panels are often so treated.

JOINTS

Joints are sometimes classified as glued, tongued, and dry joints, but it may serve better if they are described according to the use to which they are put and the positions in which they are found.

" END-ON " JOINTS are both dry and glued. These are mostly flooring joints, also known as butt or square joints; for fuller description of which see p. 27, vol. ii, and Fig. 211, vol. iii.

GROOVED AND TONGUED has a fixed tongue planed on one board to fit into a groove in the other. The tongue should be cut nearer the bottom surface than the top, to allow for wear.

DOWELLED JOINT is as shown in Fig. 50, vol. ii, the joint being a straight joint assisted by hard wood circular pins or dowels fixed at intervals. This joint is generally glued.

MATCHED JOINT.—Matched lining or boarding will be found described as " match V-jointed " or matched and beaded. The joint is practically a continuous mortise and tenon cut along the length of the two boards, and the descriptive term has reference to the finish of the edges which are either chamfered or beaded. This jointing is used in ledged doors and sheating generally.

PLOUGHED AND TONGUED JOINT has a groove cut along the edge of each adjoining board and a cross tongue or galvanised iron tongue is inserted into one groove when the other board is driven up to it, so that the tongue fits into the groove on that board and the joint made tight. This form makes a very satisfactory flooring joint if the tongue is fixed nearer the under surface than the upper to allow for wear.

REBATED AND FILLETED JOINT.—In this a rebate is cut along the under edge of both boards, the fillet placed therein resting on the joist underneath. It may be more satisfactorily used in double floorings, as the under floor prevents the fillet from sagging. It is then very useful for floors where heavy wear is expected, allowing the maximum thickness of floor board over the fillet.

REBATED JOINT.—In this the boards have their edges shot with a rebating plan, one fitting into the other, reversed as shown. This is a useful joint for flooring where secret nailing is desired to prevent the boards twisting.

REBATED, GROOVED AND TONGUED is a more intricate form of the above and suitable for the same purpose.

There is yet another form not much used, known as the *tongue and lip* joint in which the upper face of the tongue is bevelled.

SPLAYED, REBATED AND TONGUED JOINT is another form of the last.

STRAIGHT JOINTS are the simplest form of jointing boards, requiring only that the edges should be shot true. It is used in jointing any two boards where greater width is desired, when glue is used. In cheaper forms of flooring boards are laid in this manner, which is really butting and depending only upon side pressure at the time of laying. The disadvantage of flooring laid in this manner is that with further drying of the boards and consequent shrinkage the joints open, offering slits for the collection of dust.

ANGLE JOINTS—DOVETAILS

More truly belonging to joinery are those joints used in angular junctions of two boards.

CORNER LOCK is used in jointing boxes of cheap construction. It is a machine-cut joint, quickly sawn and easy to fit together, consisting of rectangular square teeth on one board fitting into equal-sized and spaced notches on the other. The joint depends for its strength on pressure and the friction of the rough sides of the tongues and notches. Glue may be used but is generally not.

PLAIN DOVETAIL JOINT is the basis of most of the angle joints used in joinery and cabinet making. The principle of the teeth and notches is the same as in that last described, but the teeth are cut wedge-shaped to resist pull in the direction away from the board in which the notches are cut. These notches consequently have their greatest width on their inner edge and diminish to their smallest width on the outer edge. Glue may be used, but if work is accurately cut should not be required.

A joint of this type, but of a cheaper nature and used where a thin board is required to be jointed to a thicker, as with the thin side of a drawer to the thicker back and front, has in the case of the back only two notches cut and spaced as far apart as possible to prevent splitting. In the case of the front very narrow teeth and notches are cut, being similarly spaced apart as far as possible.

LAP DOVETAIL JOINT.—For the purpose of concealing the joint last described used in the fronts of drawers the teeth are not cut through to the outer face of the front of the drawer, but a strip is left the entire depth of the drawer front. The same effect is gained where veneer is used by allowing the veneer to project over and conceal the joint.

MITRE DOVETAIL JOINT.—This is used for finished box work or in cabinet making where both boards show on the surface. Both the board on which the teeth are cut, and also that on which the notches are pierced have a projecting lap which is mitred. The only jointing then visible is a plain angle mitre running down the corner of the box. This, combined with a *feathered mitre* which has a strip run down a groove cut in the faces of the mitred laps, form an excellent joint which cannot pull apart, and the angle is thus prevented from gaping.

SQUARE CUT ANGLE JOINTS

BUTT JOINT.—This is the simplest form of jointing angles, and is really no joint at all, depending on nailing for its adhesion, and has no strength to resist pressure across the right angle formed by the joint. To aid slightly in this last a *rebated butt* is used in which one board is cut away to receive the entire end of the other board, and so to provide a slight shoulder and right angle to resist side pressure.

GROOVED AND TONGUED JOINT.—In this, also a refinement of the two foregoing, a groove is cut in one board into which the tongue of the rebate cut on the inner side of the other board is fitted. This binder acting as a stiffener has the additional effect of preventing a straight opening appearing from outside to inside should the boards pull away from one another.

BEADED ANGLES.—These are a form of finish applied to a rebated butt joint, the bead assisting in further concealing the joint. They may be either *rebated and beaded.*

MITRE CUT ANGLE JOINTS

PLAIN MITRE has the edges of both boards cut at an angle of 45°. The joint has no particular strength, and is really only a basis for the forms of mitred joint which follow.

FEATHERED MITRE.—This is a joint become more and more used

in almost all kinds of angle jointing met with in joinery. It consists of grooves cut in the splayed faces and a feather or strip of hardwood either driven in or placed in position. By this the joint is pulled together.

Another method of holding the mitre is that known as the *keyed mitre,* in which the plain mitre has hardwood keys let into the angle at right angles to its upright dimension. Keys are generally thin strips glued and driven into saw cuts.

The *mitre and butt* joint and *mitre and rebate* joint are adaptations to the mitre of the principles involved in *rebated and grooved and tongued* as described for use with the butt joint. They are met with in vertical walls of panelling.

WINDOWS

Generally.—The frames and sashes formed of wood used in buildings, though of various forms, all belong to either of two classes : *Solid or Casement* and *Boxed or Sash.*

SASH OR CASEMENT ?—At the outset it may be said that much worry is often caused to the intending builder by the difficulty in coming to a decision which of these two forms should be used. However, a great deal of this uncertainty might be saved if the essential fact were realised that this is not so much a matter of taste as of design. It is in fact a matter of style ; for casement windows are suitable in styles where sash would be out of place and *vice versa.* Broadly, it might be said that whilst the sash belongs to the Georgian period, the casement is in place with any design approaching the Queen Anne. Which is to an extent the same thing as saying that the sash rightly belongs to the more pretentious design and the casement to the more homely.

However, there is and probably will remain a preference for sash windows for various reasons. To the builder the greater economy will appeal, and the building owner will be prejudiced in favour of the sash on account of an imagined safeguard against the weather. He will feel, and with some justice, that a sash can be kept partly open in bad weather with a more comfortable result than can a casement. This is no doubt true of the casement that is side hung to open outwards ; but as is shown later, casements may be hung in a variety of ways.

BARS OR NO BARS ?—An even more heatedly contested bone of contention will be whether the window, sash or casement, should have bars dividing the glazing into panes. It must be agreed that whilst there will be a majority amongst architects who favour bars, there will also be a majority amongst building owners who prefer no bars. The point should be recognised, and the designer will be wise who thrashes the subject out thoroughly before starting on his design ; for the settlement, whichever way it may go, will affect the design ; and a client temporarily convinced against his will is a person with a lifelong grievance against the architect who persuaded him. Very rightly the client will claim that he lives inside his house and not outside, and that as a consequence his comfort within, to which he will claim the view from his windows goes far to contribute, is of more importance to him than the correctness of the design of his house from the outside.   There is much in the contention. But at the same time it should perhaps be realised that whilst in isolated sites where there are no other houses in view, and consequently it is natural scenery alone which meets the eye, yet the majority of houses are not so situated.   On the contrary, the majority of houses are built actually facing rows of others, and in such a position external design becomes a matter of very great importance to the comfort of the trained eye.   Design of streets is improving it is true ; but there still remain many positions in which bars as a hindrance to view from within could be looked upon in no other way than as an advantage.   And of their advantage from without there can be no real doubt.   However, as has been said, the designer will be wise who is not too obstinate in pushing his convictions in this.

PROPORTION IN DESIGN.—With or without bars, the main factor in the design of window spaces will always be the proportion of the voids to the solids in the wall areas.   Further, to insert tall and narrow window openings most suitable constructively to sashes in the walls of a building which is broad and low is obviously bad design.   And in this the designer should be guided, as in everything else, firstly by the constructive needs of his design.

CLASSES

All windows belong to either of two classes, *Solid* or *Cased* ; which names originate from the construction of the frames in which they operate.   All frames are solid, the sash being either hinged or hung to slide up and down or sideways.   But the distinguishing feature between the two classes is the necessity for the formation of a case or box for the counter-balancing weights used with sash which lift up and down.   This also explains the name *Boxed* frames, that is applied alternatively to *Cased* windows.

Frames are usually made of Baltic pine and the sills of oak ; where better workmanship is required, oak, teak or pitch pine is used instead of deal for the heads, joints and linings, and teak for the sills.   The sash of both kinds of windows are generally made of deal, though oak is used in better-class work.

Boxed or *Cased* frames have two sash supported one above the other, hung by means of sash cords run over pulley wheels fixed in the pulley stiles, and attached to lead or iron weights which work up and down in the box or case formed behind the pulley stile.   They are further defined as single or double hung, according to whether one or both of the sash are hung to slide.

TYPES

Windows consist of the following types, the sash being more or less the same in construction in all types, the difference being in the method of hanging :

Side hung to open outwards ; side hung to open inwards ; pivoted top and bottom ; pivoted centrally at side ; bottom hung to open inwards ;

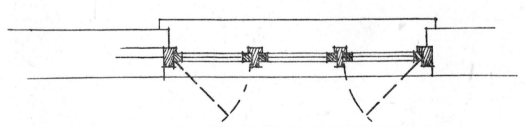

FIGS. 42 AND 43.—SIDE-HUNG CASEMENT TO OPEN OUTWARDS.

top hung to open outwards. Other forms of casement are : bull's-eye frame, circular centre hung ; hopper frame ; sliding frames or Yorkshire lights ; dormer windows ; skylights ; lantern lights.

All types of casement windows are hung in solid frames formed out

FIG. 44.—SEMICIRCULAR BAY CASEMENTS, OPENING OUTWARDS.

FIG. 45.—CASEMENTS OPENING INWARDS.

The sill requires especial attention, and a metal water bar of the type shown in Fig. 52 is employed.   This consists of a $1\frac{1}{2}''$ brass or galvanised bar extending across the width of the opening, and, being hinged, it lies flat when not in use.   Another method of effect-ing the same purpose is shown in Fig. 53, where the bottom of the sash is throated and chamfered and the sill or tran-soms   check-throated   and grooved, the groove being pierced with one or more holes in its length to allow the pas-sage of water outwards.

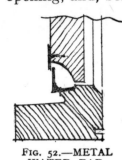

FIG. 52.—METAL
WATER BAR.

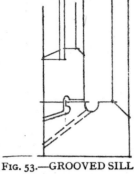

FIG. 53.—GROOVED SILL

When casements are hung to open outwards, the same degree of difficulty in excluding the weather is not experienced.   As shown in Fig. 54, the sill is throated and into the outer face of the bottom of the sash a moulded weather bar, throated

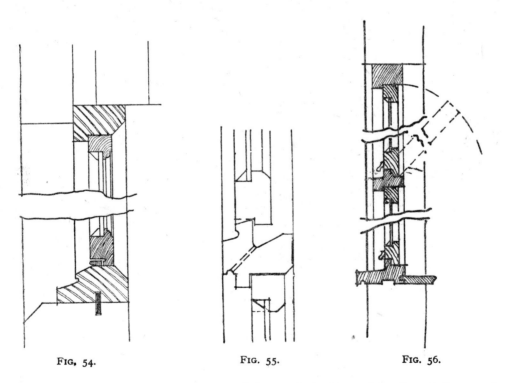

FIG. 54.   FIG. 55.   FIG. 56.

underneath, is sunk. The bottom of the sash is also splayed and throated. The sill is also bored as last described. Alternatively a metal water bar with its upper edge turned over is made to serve the purpose.

CASEMENTS PIVOTED AT TOP AND BOTTOM.—The method is here the

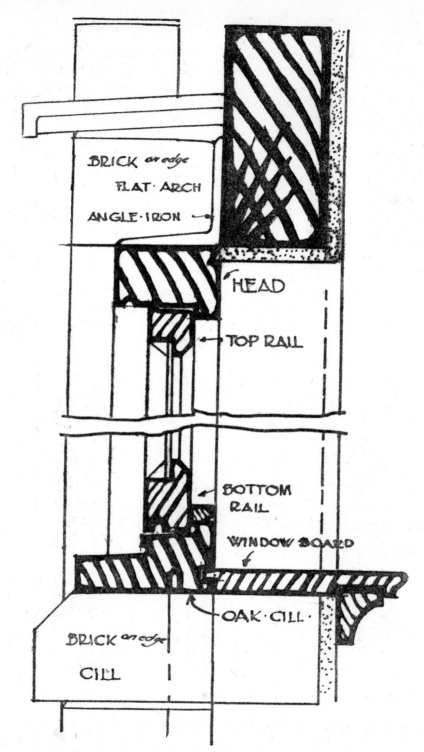

BRICK *or edge*

FLAT · ARCH

ANGLE · IRON

HEAD

TOP RAIL

BOTTOM RAIL

WINDOW BOARD

OAK · CILL ·

BRICK *or edge*

CILL

FIG. 57.—DETAIL OF CASEMENT OPENING OUTWARDS.

same as that for sashes when pivot hung at the sides, with the difference that in side-hung casements the pivot is fixed to the frame from ½″ to 1″ above the centre, whereas in top and bottom pivoting the pivot is, of course, fixed centrally. In side-hung sash the frames and sash have stop-beads cut in half and splayed, one half being fixed to the sash and the other half to the frame, whilst with the sash pivoted at top and bottom one half of the bead is fixed on the outside of the top and bottom of the sash and the other half on the inside corresponding halves, being fixed to head and sill so as to make a continuous bead when the window is closed.

The top and bottom pivoted sash is perhaps the most convenient of all for cleaning, and the centre-hung-at-sides method is suitable for transom lights at a height out of reach. In these circumstances, the portion of the sash below the pivot being greater than that above enables the window opened by cords to close itself by aid of the force of gravity when the cord is released.

CASEMENTS BOTTOM HUNG TO OPEN INWARDS and top hung to open outwards are usually employed with transom lights, as the method is useful in enabling some portion of the window to be opened in bad weather.

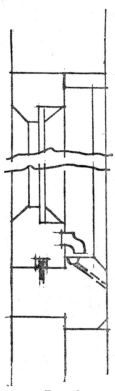

FIG. 58.

The construction of the bottom-hung casement opening inwards offers no special difficulty so far as the top is concerned, the

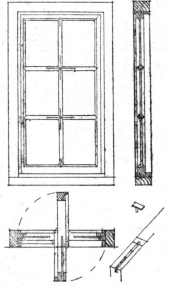

FIG. 59.—PIVOTED TOP
AND BOTTOM.

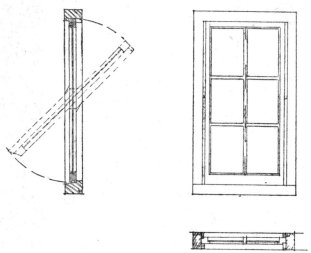

FIG. 60.—PIVOTED AT SIDES.

CONSTRUCTION OF SOLID FRAME

As already explained, solid frames are rebated inside or outside to receive the sash, or a stop may be nailed on to serve the same purpose. The sill, which is of hardwood, is bevelled, weathered and throated, occasionally being double throated.   The stiles are tenoned into the sills, and heads mortised to receive them, and the tenons are pegged with hardwood pegs.

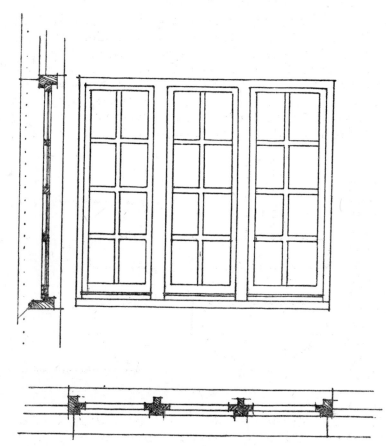

FIG. 65.—SOLID FRAME HUNG SASH.

SHUTTERS

Shutters are fixed both inside and outside, though the former are not much used in woodwork in modern times. Where inside shutters are desired they are generally of metal for protection against burglary, wooden shutters being a survival of times when construction gave less protection against draught than is customary now.

Inside shutters may be hung *folding* or *sliding*. With folding shutters the method employed is leaves hinged together to fold back into a recess formed between the inside lining of the frame and the architrave to receive them.   The inside faces of the shutters are frequently moulded or bead flush panelled, and the panel on the outer leaf, which shows during the day when the shutter is folded back, is moulded to match the architrave and lining.

SLIDING SHUTTERS may either move sideways or up and down, in which latter case they are termed lifting shutters, and are hung in the same way as lifting sash.   The lifting sash of the shutters slides down

FIGS. 66, 67.—SQUARE BAY CASEMENTS, INSIDE AND OUT.

FIG. 68.—SPECIAL PURPOSE CASEMENTS.

into a rectangular well formed in the wall to receive them and have their upper rails level with the window sill, the window board being formed into a hinged lid to conceal them when open.

Sliding shutters which operate horizontally are only possible internally where there is space for them on either side of the window. But externally they are fixed in rebated wood runners, and may be fitted with wheel bearings if required.

Outside shutters hung folding like doors are hinged to the window frame, and are suitable for either lifting sash or casements opening inwards; but they cannot be used with casements opening outwards, though they are sometimes so shown, when they become ornamental fixtures, movable only with the aid of a ladder.

Double Sash.—For positions very exposed to the weather and for the exclusion of noise windows are constructed double, having either casements to open outwards hinged to the outside of the frame of either lifting sash or casements to open inwards. The outer casement should be rebated all round as an additional preventive.

Sash for Special Purposes

A Bull's-Eye Frame is a circular sash pivoted at the ends of the hori-zontal axis, or in some cases it may be top and bottom pivoted.

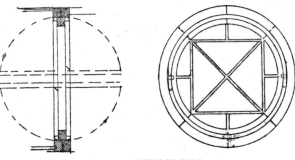

FIG. 69.—BULL'S-EYE.

As shown in Fig. 69, the frame is a double ring, each built up of three pieces breaking joint. The sash similarly is made in three pieces with butt joints and bolted together. At the point of pivoting a plane surface is made which must equal in length the thickness of the two frames or the sash and two beads. The upper part of the inner bead is attached to the upper half of the sash, which falls inwards, and the outer bead has its lower part attached to the lower part of the sash. The sash is fitted in, and the beads temporarily bradded on to the sash. A straight edge is next laid across it, parallel with the line passing through the centre. A line equal in length to the thickness is then drawn at right angles at each side. Then the segment is cut off through both beads and sash. These pieces are then glued to the centre of the frame and the pivots fixed to them.

Hospital Lights or Hopper Frames are constructed in an ordinary square rebated frame, filled in with several rebated fan-lights fixed one above the other. The fan-lights are pivoted at their lower corners into the frame, side pivots being screwed on the face of the lights. The lights when open rest on beads fixed at both sides of the jamb linings, and open independently.   The purpose of this form is to admit air in an upward direction and to prevent any downward draught direct upon the patients.

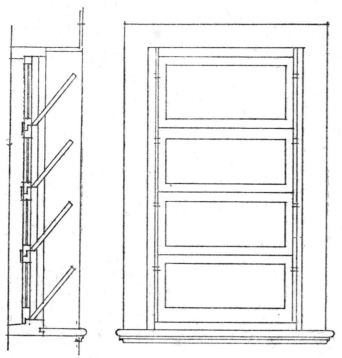

FIG. 70.—HOSPITAL LIGHTS.

YORKSHIRE LIGHTS are long, low windows having one or more sashes fitted to slide horizontally.   Where one sash only slides, the other half is glazed direct into the frame. The principle may be extended, and where three lights are desired, the middle one is generally made the movable one.   The movable sash slides over a bar let into the sill, and the head is kept in position by a bead fixed to the head of the frame. The mullion to the fixed light is rebated to fit a rebate on the meeting stile of the sliding sash when closed ; and the metal bar is also run up the inside of the outer frame, to break the joint between the sliding sash and frame.

DORMER WINDOWS

When it is desired to use the space in the roof in such a way that part of the ceiling is sloping, vertical studding is fixed at a position to give a convenient height for a sill level ; the roof is trimmed to the size desired, and a vertical light fitted therein, which, when roofed either with flat

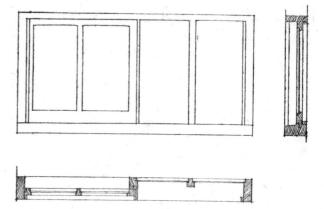

FIG. 71.—YORKSHIRE LIGHTS.

rafters or pitched at the same angle as the roof to form a small gable, is known as a dormer window.   Dormer windows may, of course, be

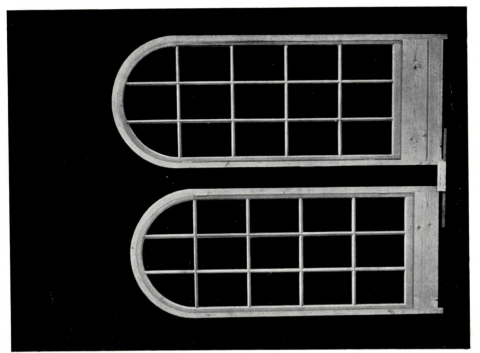

Fig. 73.—FRENCH WINDOWS WITH SEMICIRCULAR HEADS.

[c.j.—iii.

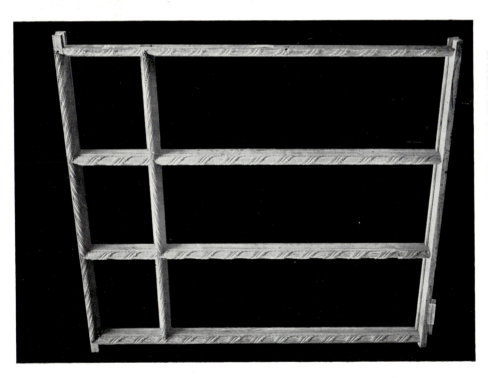

Fig. 72.—FRENCH WINDOWS WITH TRANSOMS.

fitted with any of the types of windows described, cased sash sliding or casement frames.

In cheaper work, and where insufficient attention is given to design, the frames are fitted direct to the upright studs which form the sides

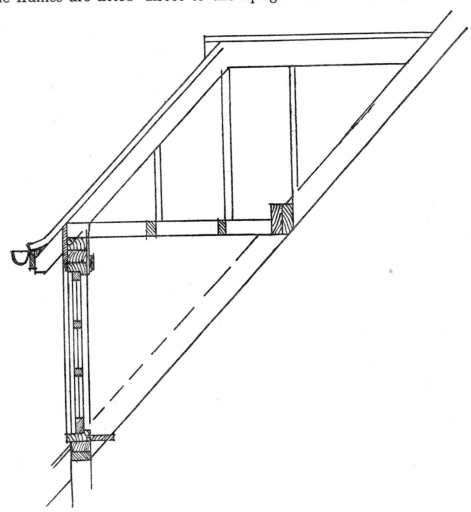

SECTION

FIG. 74.—DORMER WINDOW.

or cheeks of the dormer ; but a more pleasing effect, less skimped in appearance, will be given if the framing is continued and the opening made wider than just that bare distance required by the frame.

The trimming of the roof for dormer windows, though properly belonging to the carpenter, is described here in order that its relation to the joinery may be the better appreciated. Across the top of the opening to take the feet of the cut rafters a trimmer is inserted tusk-tenoned to the two rafters which bound the opening at its sides.   These rafters, which must be of stouter scantling than the others, on account of the additional weight conveyed to them by the trimmer, are termed *trimming rafters*.   The cut rafters are called *trimmed rafters*.   As has been said, from the floor, resting on the floor boards or joists, upright short lengths of studs, known as ashlaring, are cut in and halved to the common rafters to form the vertical face.   Where these studs come directly under the window-sill two lengths of rafter, known as the lower trimmers, are tusk-tenoned into the trimming rafters at either end, and the uprights are stub-tenoned into them.   On this lower trimmer the sill is placed and nailed thereto.   The upright stud in the lower angle of the opening and at the end of the lower trimmer is halved over the trimming rafter and carried up to give a fixing for the frame, and it is this corner stud which is often allowed to form the angle of the dormer window, whereas, as has been said, a double stud with a few inches' space between, faced with a panel or corner tile hanging, gives a better appearance.   This is very simply done by halving on to the other side of the trimming rafter a second upright stud which then forms the angle.

The triangular sides of the dormer, or cheeks, are framed by means of short lengths of studding generally halved on to the insides of the trimming rafters, but preferably to the outside to line with the second angle studs just described.

The dormer may be flat roofed with joists lengthened, resting on capping pieces, which terminate the upright cheek studs ; or rafters cut to a pitch may be bird's-mouthed to or notched over them.   On these upright faces or cheeks boarding is hung and covered either with lead, lath and plaster, or tile hanging.   Where the last is used, it will be seen that the widened surface at the side of the frame referred to is of special advantage.   The tiles may then be finished behind the panel or the panel omitted when space is found for angle tiling, and the joint between this and the frame may be covered by an angle mould.

Alternatively a solid post may be erected at the angle, as was often done in old work, the post being heavily moulded ; but the method is now found to be too expensive as a general thing.

Within the framing so constructed the sash or casement frame is fitted, having fascia boards or moulding in the angles to conceal the joint between the frame and studs.   This fascia may be carried along over the head of the window, or a moulded cornice may be fixed to the ends of the rafters.   When a flat roof is desired, it must in practice have a slight slope for drainage towards the front when the top members of the cornice should be formed of a rain-water gutter, half round or moulded.

SKYLIGHTS are sashes fixed into a well opening framed in the roof, when the light is at the same slope as the roof in distinction from lantern

FIG. 76.—LIFTING SASH, TWO-PANE LIGHTS.

[C.J.—III.

FIG. 75.—CASEMENT TO OPEN OUT, WITH TRANSOM.

64]

lights, which are larger in construction, either on a flat roof or cutting the ridge of a pitched roof.

Two trimmers are inserted in between trimming rafters to carry the ends of the trimmed rafters, and a *lining* or *curb* is then fixed to these and to the face of the trimming rafters. The curb is lined with a thin facing which is beaded at its lower angle, and has a check cut in its back to receive the plaster of the ceiling. The curb should be of whatever depth that it is required that the well should be, and never less than to give the frame of the skylight about 3″ rise above the line of the roof, as the opening must be flashed round outside with lead and these must be sufficient height to form a satisfactory gutter for rain-water descending the roof. The frame of the skylight rests on this 2″ lining, and when hinged is hinged at the upper end.

The stiles of the skylight are $2\frac{1}{4}″$ and the bottom rail $1\frac{1}{4}″$, the bottom rail being throated and should overhang the curb. The reason for the bottom rail being made of thinner stuff than the top and sides is in order that the glass may be continued over the rail to prevent the entrance of rain-water. The glass is secured to the bottom

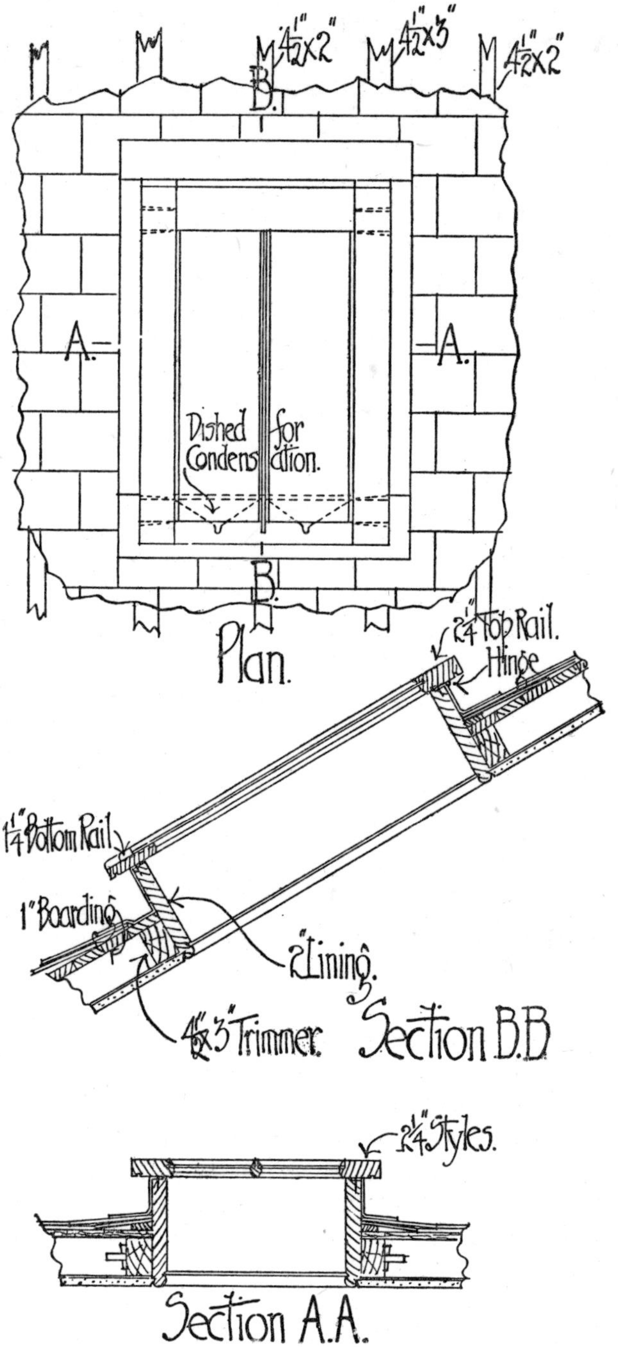

FIG. 77.—SKYLIGHT.

C.J. III—5

rail by copper clips and grooved into the top and side rails. A dishing must be made under the tail of each pane of glass to permit the escape of condensed vapour on the under surface of the glass.

LANTERN LIGHTS consist of upright glazed framings with glazed pitch and hipped roofs. They may be fitted to flats or pitched roofs, and serve the purpose of giving top light where such is specially desired. They may be either square or rectangular in plan, and are sometimes formed polygonal and circular. The framing of the roof consists of the insertion of a stout curb to carry the uprights of the lantern fitted into the trimmed opening. On the curb is fixed the oak sill, and generally bolted thereto and having a continuous water bar to break the joint let into the sill and curb. The sill projects over the outside face of the curb for 3″ to 4″ to give room for throating and an overhang ; and it is also projected inside for a sufficient length to enable the lining of the well to be housed into a groove cut in its underside. The sill should be double checked and throated, and grooved underneath for the lead flashing over the curb to be turned up into it.

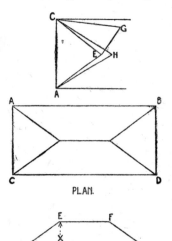

PLAN.

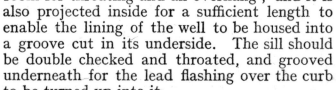

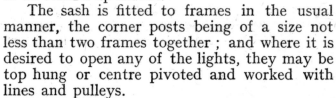

ELEVATION
FIG. 78.

The sash is fitted to frames in the usual manner, the corner posts being of a size not less than two frames together ; and where it is desired to open any of the lights, they may be top hung or centre pivoted and worked with lines and pulleys.

The glazing and frame of the upper pitched portion is similar to that described for sky- lights, with the exception that they meet at the centre and are cut splayed to fit against a ridge, over which a lead roll is fixed.

As a difficulty may be sometimes ex- perienced in determining the lengths of hip rafters, the simplest method of obtaining these, together with the lengths of the sash bars, is here given, in Fig. 78.

Let ABCD represent the plan of roof, and CEFD the elevation. In neither case is the *true* length of the hip rafter indicated. Draw a plan of one end, as shown by AEC. From E draw a line at right angles to EC, and mark off the distance on same to G, equal to the vertical height EG on elevation. CG is then the length required, and the isosceles triangle AHC, with AC as base and the length CG as sides, is the true shape of the end of the roof. Lines parallel to this triangle at the correct thickness will represent the sash framing, and the lengths of the sash bars may be found by setting out their positions along AC and drawing perpendiculars from them.

The method of obtaining the correct bevel of hip, or, as it is technically called, the *backing*, may also be given. It is very necessary that these bevels be true, so that they may lie in the same planes as the sides and ends of the roof.   Let BFD in Fig. 79 represent the plan of one end as before.   Draw FK at right angles to FD, and in length equal to the vertical height between the top and bottom of the hip.   Join KD, and from any point L erect a perpendicular to it, cutting FD at M.   From M draw a line at right angles to FD, cutting BD at N.   From M, with ML as radius, mark the point O ; join NO, when the angle NOM will be the required bevel.   The best method of ensuring watertightness is to finish with a roll covered with lead and dressed down over the top bars of sashes, as shown in Fig. 80.

Parts of a Sash Window

The construction of a single sash window with both upper and lower sash hung to open and the names of the various parts are as follows and illustrated in Fig. 81 accompanying.

The box, being the main feature, is described first, its purpose being to form a casing in which the weights which counterbalance the sash operate ; the principle of the sash window consisting of sash hung in frames by means of weights run over pulley wheels, and of such a weight as the sash may be raised to any position and there remain in equilibrium.   The box which contains the weights, as shown in the plan, is framed up with a *pulley stile*, A, which is rebated into the linings, *inner* B and *outer* C, in the manner shown.   Along the back of the box and against the wall a thin strip

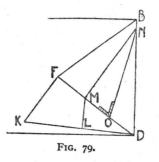

FIG. 79.

is fixed to complete the box and termed the *back lining*, D.   A *parting strip*, E, for the purpose of preventing the weights from jambing together, completes the interior of the box.

The *head*, F, is framed similarly, but without the back lining, and is blocked as shown.   The *pulley wheels*, G, are cut into the pulley stiles and fitted flush, and the weights attached to the sash, as described later, hang down inside the casing and can be reached by means of a *pocket piece*, H, if desired, as when a sash-cord breaks or the weights jamb for any reason.

The bottom sash consists of a *bottom rail*, I, which is throated and splayed on its bottom face ; and a *meeting rail*, J, which is splayed and rebated to fit the meeting rail of the top sash.   The *stiles*, K, of both sashes and cut squares at the back are kept apart by means of a strip let into a groove in the pulley stile and known as a *parting bead*, L.   The bottoms of the upper sash stiles are projected downwards for from 4″ to 6″, and terminated in a moulded horn, M.   The sill, N, is weathered and check throated, and has grooved into it a ventilating strip, O, which enables the bottom sash to be railed slightly, so that air may find its way in at

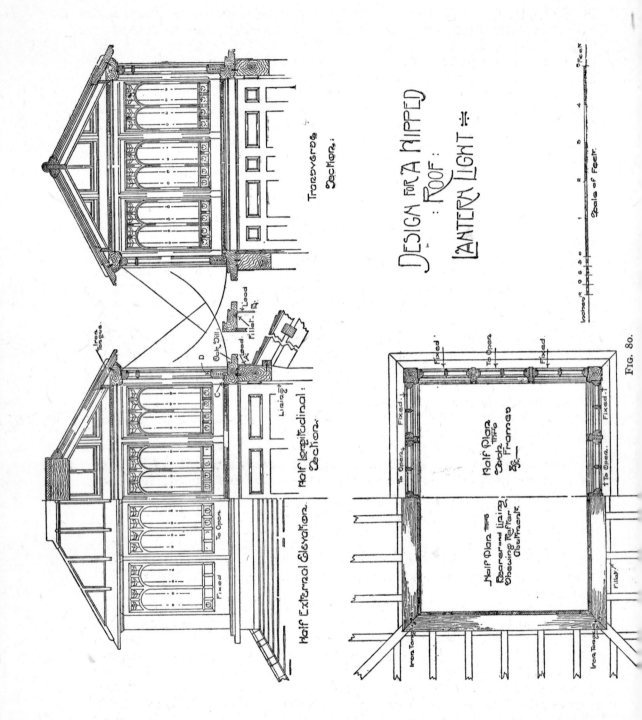

Transverse Section.

Half Longitudinal Section.

Half External Elevation.

DESIGN FOR A HIPPED
: ROOF :
LANTERN LIGHT :

Half Plan thro
Roof and Lining,
shewing Rafter
Abutment.

Half Plan thro
Sash Frames
&c.

FIG. 80.

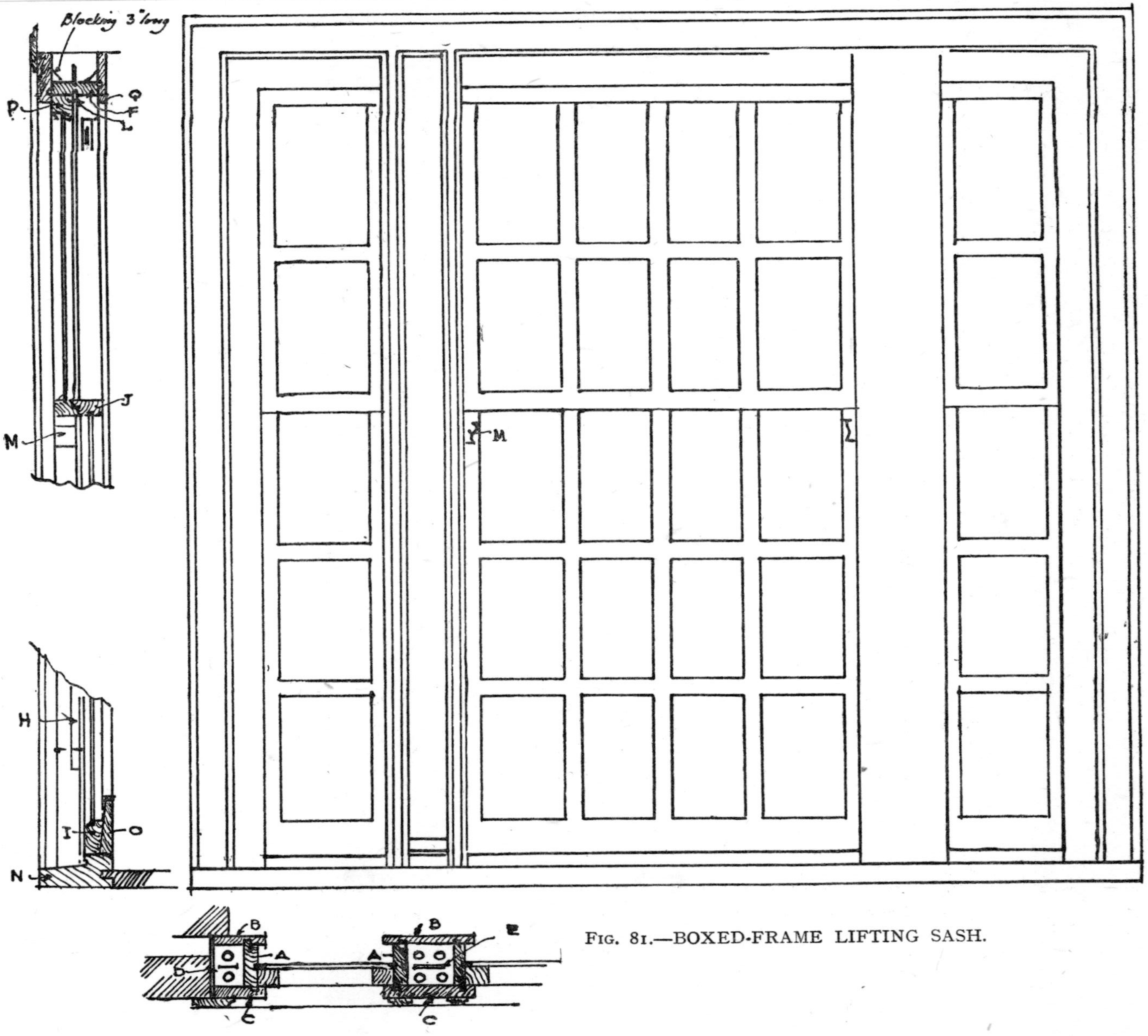

FIG. 81.—BOXED-FRAME LIFTING SASH.

four weights is not objectionable.   Besides the usual parting strips a cross lining, dividing each two sets of weights, is inserted.

A SINGLE BOXED MULLION has already been described.

SASH LINES are fixed to a fixing slot cut in a circular-headed slot, and travel in a cord groove cut in the stile, though in cheaper work they are fixed in a ploughed groove at the back of the stile by means of clout-headed nails.

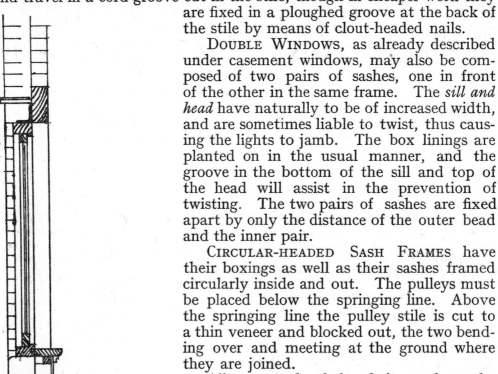

DOUBLE WINDOWS, as already described under casement windows, may also be composed of two pairs of sashes, one in front of the other in the same frame.   The *sill and head* have naturally to be of increased width, and are sometimes liable to twist, thus causing the lights to jamb.   The box linings are planted on in the usual manner, and the groove in the bottom of the sill and top of the head will assist in the prevention of twisting.   The two pairs of sashes are fixed apart by only the distance of the outer bead and the inner pair.

CIRCULAR-HEADED SASH FRAMES have their boxings as well as their sashes framed circularly inside and out.   The pulleys must be placed below the springing line.   Above the springing line the pulley stile is cut to a thin veneer and blocked out, the two bending over and meeting at the ground where they are joined.

All segment-headed sash frames have the head of the frame shaped to follow the sweep of the ridge and the sash rail is parallel.   The head is built up in the solid, the outside lining is shaped to fit the opening, but the inside lining is trimmed straight to fit under the lintel.   A sash segment headed in shape is sometimes fitted into a square-headed frame,

FIG. 84.—SECTION OF CASE-
MENT WINDOW OPENING OUT.

when the frame is made similarly to the ordinary window frames, with the exception of the outside lining, which is made to follow the curve of the sash head.   The outside lining and the top rail of the sash have their end edges shaped to correspond with the sweep of the ridge.

SINGLE SLIDING SASH FRAME.—Where walls are of thin construction a single lifting sash with a hinged transom light, made to open in the manner of a fanlight, is used.   The bottom sash is raised by means of the fanlight being opened outwards, the pulley being fixed as near as possible to the top of the hinged fanlight to enable the lower sash to be raised to its greatest extent.   The meeting joint of the rails between a lifting sash and the hinged casement is bevelled, and the outside of the joint covered by a metal bar.   It will be necessary to cut away a groove in the fanlight to clear the sash cords, and the outside lining is cut away to permit passage of the fanlight.   The piece cut off is fixed on the outside of the sash for the sake of appearance, but it must be terminated to give clearance at the top to the outside lining.

SLIDING AND REVOLVING SASH WINDOWS are specially designed to enable the sashes whilst sliding in the ordinary manner alternatively to be revolved and brought down to a position where they are more easily reached for the purpose of cleaning the outsides.

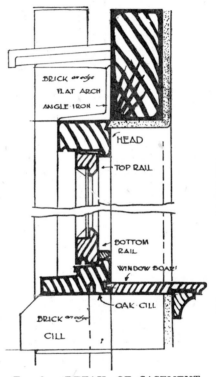

A SLIDING AND SWINGING SASH is a method of converting the ordinary double-hung sash window into a casement window.   The frame is of the usual construction, and the device may be fitted to existing windows.   The stiles are made in two sections, one containing the glass and the other being attached to the weight cords.   These are rebated together.   At one side of the frame the two parts of the stiles are hinged together with ordinary butt hinges.   The striking stiles are connected by a pair of locking plates, one being attached to the sliding stile and containing a slot or pocket into which a lead or projection formed upon the other plate slips when the two are brought together.   When it is desired to release the sash, all that is necessary to do is to hold the sliding sash with one hand in order to prevent the sash weight

FIG. 85.—DETAIL OF CASEMENT SECTION.

lifting it, and at the same time lift the sash slightly when the two plates engage and the sash is free to swing inwards or outwards.

BAY-WINDOWS

Bay-windows may be fitted with either cased or solid frames.   Their purpose lies in the desire to obtain additional light by a window which, on account of the angles at which some of the sides are formed, occupies less wall space than if the same number of lights were built flat in the wall.   Also they are useful when it is desired to obtain an oblique view from within a room as well as that which would be possible from a window in one plane.

pane lights one on either side. Combinations of almost any type desired may be designed, so long only as the modulus of the window pane be kept.

This matter is of importance to the ultimate appearance of the building generally; but it will be the deciding factor in the proportions of a bay window.

FIG. 88.—COMPOSITE WINDOWS.

Some idea of the projection desired having been gathered and the style of the design of the building determining the shape and number of sides of the bay, it will remain to choose a composite form that will fit in.

As the construction is the same for all, a simple three-sided bay has been taken for illustration, and this is shown fitted with a composite boxed frame, and also with casements, the principles being the same for both.

For the lifting sash a composite sash has been chosen for the front wall of the bay, having a three-pane window in the centre and a one-pane window on either hand; whilst the angle walls each have a two-pane light.

A point of great importance to the appearance of any bay is that rather than that the wood frame should be fitted flush up against the face of the main wall of the house, it should be separated from that wall by a nib of brickwork at least 4½", formed on the angle wall. This prevents the feeling

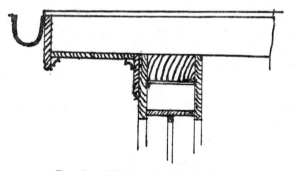

FIG. 89.—HEAD OF FLAT BAY.

that a hole was left in the main wall, and the bay fitted in, and gives in place the idea that the bay is part of the necessary construction.

The angles, where boxed, may finish upon the wood sill which is continuous all round the bay, or a better appearance may be given by boxing round a wood angle post which is run down to the damp course level.

The head of the bay may be flat, or hipped, or domed, and in any case the same principles apply. Fig. 89 shows the method where a flat-roofed bay is desired. Over the boxed frame a plate is fixed on to which the rafters are spiked and being projected from the face of the frame have a fascia run along their ends, and to this the gutter is fixed. A soffit of board is cut in under these rafters, and cover mouldings are added to fill in the angles and to form a panelled soffit.

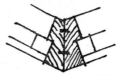

FIG. 90.—BAY ANGLE FOR CASEMENTS.

Where casements are desired in the bay-window, the size of bay and number of windows having been decided upon as before, and as before

FIG. 91.—SASH BAY ANGLE.

the pane being the modulus, the brick nib being constructed on the angle of the main wall as before, the angle post may either be boxed, as in Fig. 91, or built in solid, and either terminated on the wood sill or carried down to the damp course, all as described for the sash window. But it should be noted that where heavy construction is desired, and the bay-window carries a weight above the size of the timber forming the angle post in consequence being large, it will be found preferable to substitute a metal column and to box round it as indicated, as posts cut out of the solid will shift and crack vertically as the timber dries out. The dwarf wall between the posts will be filled in with brickwork, and the posts should have either a rebated face at that point for the brickwork to fit into, or they should be grooved for a metal water bar fixed vertically, or lead strip turned in behind the brickwork and let into the post.

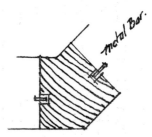

FIG. 92.—SOLID BAY ANGLE.

BAY-WINDOW DETAILS

A CASEMENT BAY.—An alternative method of framing the angle posts of a casement bay-window is shown in Fig. 91, where the jambs

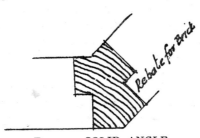

FIG. 93.—SOLID ANGLE.

consist of two parts splayed at the back to give the required angle, and jointed with a wood tongue let into a groove cut in the splayed face of each, the two parts being screwed together; the joint at the angle being concealed by a cover mould. The jambs are tenoned and wedged into the head and sill. The upper lights are hung at the top to open outwards, the transom being weathered and rebated, and is tenoned into the jambs and mullions and secured with bolts. The head is halved together, and the mullions are stub-tenoned into it and secured with coach screws. The sills are mitred, and the joints cross-tongued, and fixed with a handrail bolt painted with red lead.

SASH BAY DETAILS.—The angle posts are here formed of the sash weight casings formed as before but cut at an angle. The outer linings being jointed as shown, and finished with a staff bead on the angle. The inside linings are mitred and the joint concealed by a cover mould, cut splayed at the back to fit in the angle. The sills are connected at the angles either by halving and screwing or by a mitred joint secured with a handrail bolt. Screwed across the top of the head are short pieces of 1″ stuff. The ceiling of the bay is run from the top of the frame to the arch or beam over the opening in the main wall, and may be either plastered or panelled in wood. In the first case space must be left above the head for an architrave, into which will be housed the top lining, and will pick up and be mitred to the architrave run up the angle made by the side of the bay and the main wall : the plaster fitting down behind the architrave, as described for an ordinary bay in a plane wall. Where a panelled ceiling is required to the bay, short lengths of firring are carried from the head of the bay to the underside of the beam over the opening, and to these framed panelling is fixed ; the frame of the panelling being tongued into a groove in the head of the frame.

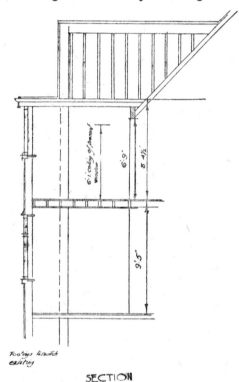

SECTION

FIG. 96.—SECTION OF BAY FORMED
BY CASEMENTS.

FRENCH CASEMENTS are glazed doors giving entrance to a room direct from the outside. They consist of a pair of doors formed like large casement windows hung to open inwards, and may be either combined with other and fixed casements of similar dimensions, or with casements or ordinary lights as shown in Figs. 94 and 95.

Where a transom light is fixed as above, the detail is the same as for a casement window, but the door head or transom is rebated above for the transom light to open outwards and underneath for the doors to open inwards.

In designing, care should be taken where bars are fitted that they should line in the doors with those in the windows, and that the panes should be of the same width ; but where this is impossible a satisfactory

FIG. 95.—FRENCH WINDOW AND CASEMENTS, WITH BARS,
COMBINED.

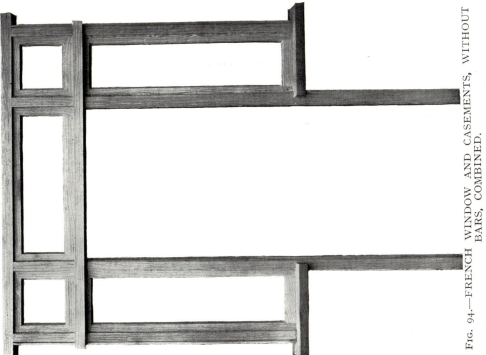

FIG. 94.—FRENCH WINDOW AND CASEMENTS, WITHOUT
BARS, COMBINED.

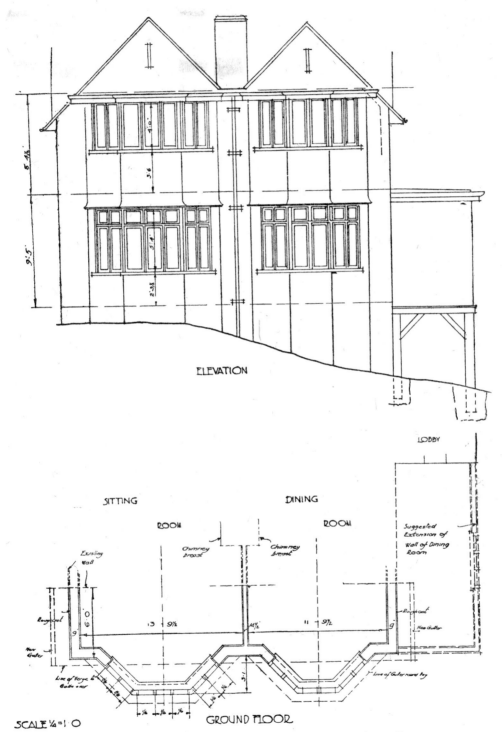

ELEVATION

SITTING ROOM

DINING ROOM

LOBBY

Suggested Extension of Wall of Dining Room

Chimney breast

Chimney breast

Existing Wall

GROUND FLOOR

SCALE ¼"=1'0"

FIG. 97.—BAYS FORMED OF CASEMENT WINDOWS.

79

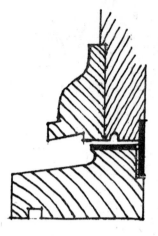

FIG. 98.

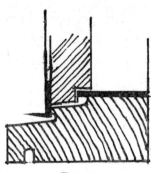

FIG. 99.

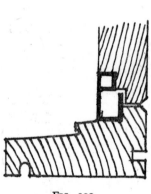

FIG. 100.

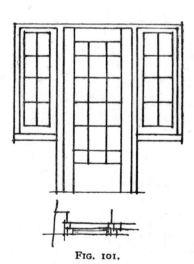

FIG. 101.

METAL WATER-BAR DETAILS.

effect may be achieved by lining the base of the inner panes and allowing the outer panes to come what size they will, if possible half panes.   These outer panes are then termed marginal lights.

The transom light is sometimes made to open inwards, though the practice is not recommended, and gives rise to considerable and unnecessary intricacy of construction to overcome the penetration of the weather.   Fig. 54 shows a method adopted for this in the transom, which is weathered and throated externally and has a groove pierced with outlet holes on its inner and upper face for the collection of the water of condensation.

The hanging stiles of the doors have cocked beads worked on the outside edge fitting into a groove in the frame or mullion.   And the meeting stiles may be cut on the splay and fitted with a hook, as the hook would cut through a single tenon.   Patent water bars of various designs are manufactured for the sills which lie flat when open, and are raised by a catch on the bottom rail and brought into action when the doors are closed.

When a metal joint is preferred to the hook bolt described for sealing the meeting stiles when closed, a patent bolt known as the Janus fastening is fitted.   This consists of a $\frac{5}{8}''$ by $\frac{1}{4}''$ copper bar fitted into a brass channelled casing, which is sunk flush in one of the rebated edges of the stile.   A corresponding grooved casing is sunk in the edge of the other stile.   On the lever handle being turned to close the door a three-way action is set up in the copper bar, which operates from the lever upwards and downwards and outwards, thus bolting top and bottom into head and sill and sealing the joint between the two meeting stiles.

METAL WEATHER BARS.—Metal weather bars of various sections have been invented for use with wood casements, but their application necessitates such an additional cost that it has become a question whether the use of the metal frame will not supersede them ; especially as in section they are practically the same as the metal casement.   And if the weather cannot be satisfactorily excluded by wood weather bars and rebatings, it would suggest that the metal frame would be preferable.

The metal weather bar of whatever type depends for its efficacy upon the formation of channels and traps for water ; whether these be formed by knife edge and plane surface or channel bends, the principle is the same.   A few of the more generally met with types are shown in the accompanying illustrations.

The accompanying figures show the more usually met with weather bars constructed of wood and sometimes used in conjunction with metal strips.   They are grooved and nailed or screwed into the bottom rail of door or window or may be splayed or moulded as shown, the under surface forming a hollow air space and the bottom being throated ; the principle underlying the throating being that a vertical face is thus formed up which the rain-water cannot climb even when driven by the wind.

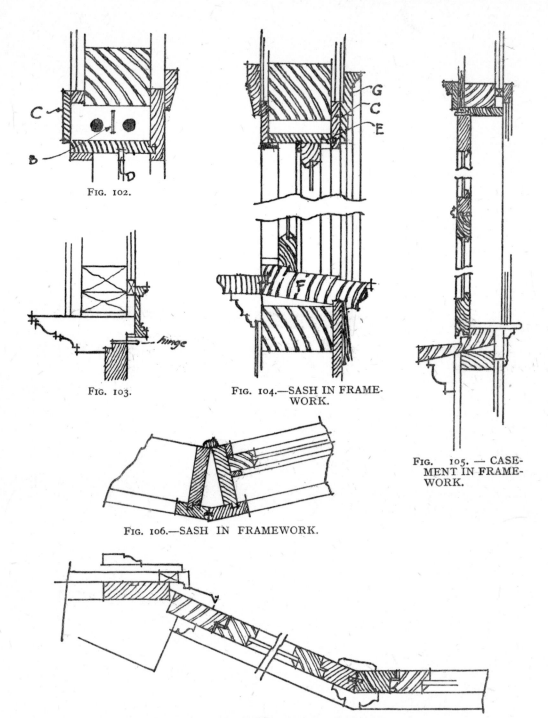

FIG. 102.

FIG. 103.

FIG. 104.—SASH IN FRAME-WORK.

FIG. 105. — CASE-MENT IN FRAME-WORK.

FIG. 106.—SASH IN FRAMEWORK.

FIG. 107.—CASEMENT IN FRAMEWORK.

WINDOW DETAILS.

WINDOWS IN FRAME CONSTRUCTION

LIFTING SASH.—Formed of *skeleton frames* in framework building in distinction from the box casings used in masonry. The main parts as shown in Figs. 102 to 106 are the same, being the pulley stile, A; the parting bead, B; the outside casing, C; the stop bead, D; and the head E, and sill, F.

In addition an outside moulding or architrave to cover the joint between the outer casing and the wall covering is nailed on to the outside casing and known as a *band moulding*, G; though in cheaper work the outside casing is made to serve this purpose also, being fixed beyond the line of the wall covering, which is fitted down behind it. The inside casing of the skeleton frame, being internally of the same dimensions as the thickness of the wall, forms part of the interior finish, and is fixed at the top to a stop, the plaster being run down behind it and finishing against the stop. In cheaper work also the tongue and grooved joint between the pulley stile and the outside casing is omitted, a butt joint being substituted and the casing simply nailed to the pulley stile.

The method of constructing the sill offers some comment, as being rather different from that used in masonry walls. As shown, it is formed with a rebate on to which the bottom sash fits and a throating is cut in the underside which projects out from the face of the wall outside, for the weather boarding shingles or other outside wall covering to fit up into. The sill itself is fitted at an angle to slope outwards and rests on a horizontal stud on its outer end and on a firred ground on its inner end. The window board is halved and nailed to the inner top edge of the sill, and forms an additional rebate for the sash to fit down into when closed.

In plan a strip, H, is attached to the edge of the outside lining to which, in countries where such are required, the fly screen may be hinged. Also there is shown in the plan a hardwood strip, I, which is let into the ground casing, J, on to which the architrave is fixed. The parting strip, in pine $\frac{3}{8}''$, is hung as to windows in solid walls from the top, so that it may be swung to one side in getting at both weights from the one pocket.

CASEMENTS IN WOOD FRAME BUILDINGS are constructed similarly to doors in stud partitions, in that in place of the 4″ by 3″ solid frames used in masonry $1\frac{3}{4}$ linings are used as frames. These extend in width for a distance equal to that of the stud plus the plaster and outside wall covering, and to the ends of the lining, and over the wall covering outside and the plaster inside, are fixed the outer and inner architraves.

Alternative methods of excluding the weather are shown by means of the half-round rebate on the hanging stile and the astragal mould on the meeting stiles. The sill is again of different detail from that used in solid work, being cut splayed on its underside and having additional fixing at its ends, being nailed to the vertical studs framing the sides of the opening left for the window to be fitted into.

For sash opening inwards the only point calling for special notice is that, on account of the inside finish used in the form of the architrave, a hinge must be fitted which provides a projection sufficient to allow the sash to clear this when opened.

BAY-WINDOWS IN FRAME BUILDINGS

CASEMENTS.—Figs. 87 and 88 show the plan of a bay in which the framing of the angle posts is of interest. The whole is of a lighter formation than that used in solid masonry, the sash and frames being $1\frac{3}{4}''$ thick, the two frames being tongued together at their splayed joint and a splayed and tongued architrave being fitted to cover the joint inside; and a solid moulded architrave is planted on the outside as shown.

SASH BALANCES.—The detail of a lifting sash corner post shows how, when it is desired to keep the corner post slight in appearance, the weights are dispensed with and sash balances substituted. This consists of a drum on which the cord is wound. The drum contains a coiled steel spring, which sustains the weight of the sash.

Sash balances are made with springs of sufficient strength to operate sash weighing up to 600 lb. and require only the thickness of a lining for their accommodation. An additional advantage of these is that they operate most strongly when the window is shut, which is often of great convenience in countries where it is customary to move frame buildings bodily from one site to another. Sash hung with spring balances must be provided with self-locking sash lifts to prevent the lower sash sliding up.

Where bay-window angles in sashed frames are required to carry great weight, a steel column or joist is built inside the casing; the outer linings being clamped thereto and the face of the angles being formed of masonry or terra-cotta. This method also enables the angle to be as small as possible. The terra-cotta facing is clamped to the steel work, and the angle between the terra-cotta and the outside lining fitted with a cover mould.

CHAPTER IV

JOINERY: DOORS AND WOOD FINISHINGS TO ROOMS

Types: Ledged and Braced; Framed and Braced; Framed and Panelled—Door Frames and Finishings—External Doors—Internal Door Linings: Plain, Framed, Double-framed and Skeleton Framed—Grounds—Framed Grounds—Architraves—Sliding Doors: In Pockets; Modern, for Garages—Special Doors: Jib Doors, Folding Doors, Cross Battened, Front Entrance, Double Margined—Data—Materials—Diminished Style Doors—Dwarf Doors—Stable Doors—Cow and Byre Doors—Patent Composite Door—Dowel-constructed Doors—Butterfly Door—Hospital Doors—Wood Finishings to Rooms: Skirtings, Dados, Panelling, Picture Rails, Friezes, Ceilings.

THE stock types of doors, upon which all forms met with in joinery are based, consist of the following: Ledged; ledged and framed; framed and braced; ledged, framed and braced; framed and panelled.

TYPES

LEDGED DOORS consist of vertical battens clinched from the face to three ledges, as shown in Fig. 76, both the ledges and battens being $1\frac{1}{4}''$ to $1\frac{1}{2}''$ in thickness and the battens being matched to prevent shrinkage. This is the cheapest form of door often met with in both old country cottage work and in the cheaper forms of house work to-day, especially in the country. The rails are termed, bottom ($9''$ by $1\frac{1}{4}''$), middle ($6''$ by $1\frac{1}{4}''$) and top rails ($4\frac{1}{2}''$ by $1\frac{1}{4}''$).

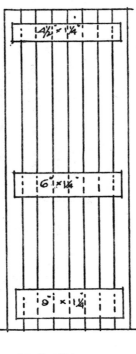

LEDGED

PLAN

FIG. 108.

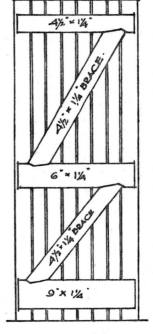

LEDGED & BRACED

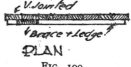

PLAN

FIG. 109.

85

LEDGED AND BRACED DOORS have braces diagonally placed to prevent drooping, the brace running from bottom rail to middle rail, and from middle rail to top rail, having their bottom ends on the side on which the door is hinged. The battens are beaded or V-jointed on one or both sides, the ledges being either cut short or bevelled on their edges or

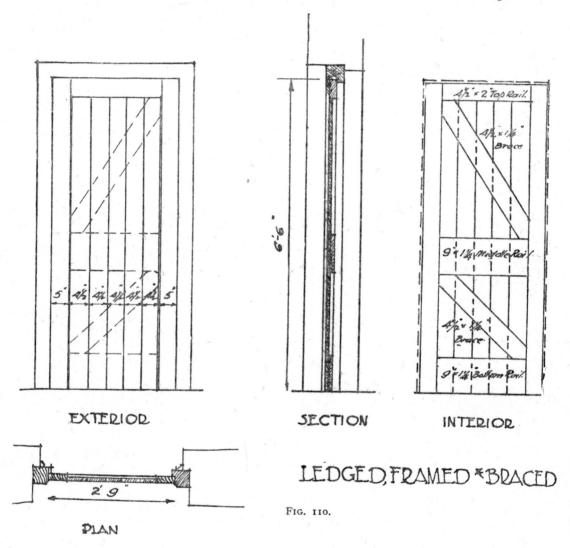

EXTERIOR   SECTION   INTERIOR

PLAN

LEDGED, FRAMED & BRACED

FIG. 110.

both to give clearance. The doors are hung with T-hinges to line with the ledges, when the doors open inwards the rebates in the frames are of a depth equal to the thickness of the battens and ledges. The bottom rail is 9″ by $1\frac{1}{4}$″, the middle rail 6″ by $1\frac{1}{4}$″, the top rail $4\frac{1}{2}$″ by $1\frac{1}{4}$″, and the braces both $4\frac{1}{2}$″ by $1\frac{1}{4}$″. The braces are let into the rails in the manner shown in Fig. 108.

Fig. 111.—MODERN TUDOR DOOR AND WINDOWS—TUDOR HOUSE, ARGYLL PLACE.
Architects, Edwin T. Hall, F.R.I.B.A., F.R.San.I., and E. Stanley Hall, M.A., F.R.I.B.A.

[c.j.—111.

FRAMED AND BRACED DOORS.—The frame consists of styles and heads being equal in thickness to the battens and braces taken together ; a bottom rail, lock rail and two braces equalling the thickness of the head less the thickness of the boarding. The boarding $\frac{3}{4}$" to $1\frac{1}{4}$" in thickness is tongued into the stiles and head, run over the lock and bottom rail and V-jointed. The edges of the head are chamfered. This type of door makes good, strong doors for external work, such as wood and coal cellars. The rails and head are tenoned and the joints should be run in with white lead or thick paint. Cross garnet or T-hinges are used to hang the doors, and should be placed either level with the ledges on the outside or on the ledges on the inside. The stiles of the frame are generally 5", and the battens from $4\frac{1}{2}$" to 3" in width. The bottom rail is 9" by $1\frac{1}{4}$", the middle rail 9" by $1\frac{1}{4}$", and top rail $4\frac{1}{2}$" by 2", the braces being $4\frac{1}{2}$" by $1\frac{1}{4}$".

FRAMED AND PANELLED DOORS.— These are practically pieces of panelling hung on hinges. In old work the spacing was equal in the doors to that in the panelling. Panelled doors consist of stock sizes, 6' 6" or 6' 8" in height, in width usually 2' 8". The type of door determines the number of panels. A six-panel door is framed out of stiles, top rail, bottom rail, and has intermediately a frieze and middle rail. The top and frieze rails are 4" deep by

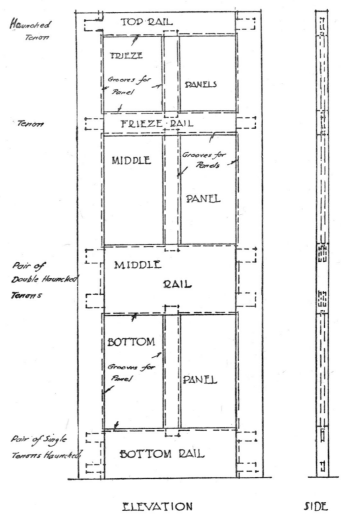

ELEVATION   SIDE

PANELLED DOOR.

FIG. 112.

$1\frac{1}{2}''$ to $2''$ in thickness, the bottom rail $8''$ to $9''$, the middle or lock rail anything from $10''$ to $1'\ 2''$. The extra width is necessitated by the

FIG. 113.

space taken up by the lock. Regard must be had to the construction and to the hanging of the lock rail at a convenient height from the floor. It should be about $2'\ 8''$ to the centre of the door handle. Lock rails are often placed at a height too great for a child to be able to open the door; in three-panel doors with a single panel at the top, this is often found to be the case, the height of $3'\ 3''$ should never be exceeded. The rails are tenoned into the stiles as shown in the details, the top rail being jointed with that form known as the hinged tenon, the frieze rail being tenoned, the bottom rail being a pair of single tenons haunched, and the middle rail having a pair of double haunched tenons. All tenons are wedged, and care should be taken to see that sufficient

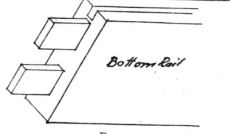

FIG. 114.

space is left on the lock rail between the tenons so that a head fixing may be gained for the mortise lock without the tenons being cut away. The upright style between the panels is termed a munting, and varies from $3''$ to $4\frac{1}{2}''$ in width. In a four-panel door the top munting is stub-tenoned into the top and middle rails and the bottom

FIG. 115.

munting into the middle and bottom rails. The rails are tenoned into the stiles before described, the top rail having one and the middle and bottom rails having generally two single tenons each, but here again double tenons should always be used where a mortise lock is fixed, when the sum of the width of the tenons equals one-third of the width of the rail. The inside edges of both stiles and top and bottom rails, and both

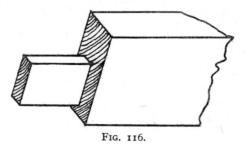

FIG. 116.

edges of the middle rail and muntings, are ploughed to receive the panels. The method of fixing is as follows: the rails and muntings are put together first. In high-class work these are fixed tenoned. The panels are next inserted, and the stiles knocked on and wedged. Glue is used in the mortise and tenon joints, and in polished hardwood doors the rails should always be fixed tenoned.

Framed and panelled doors are of the following kinds :

SQUARE AND SUNK, in which a thin panel is used and the edges of the rails and muntings are squared.

MOULDED AND SQUARED, when one side of the door is moulded and the other plain sunk.

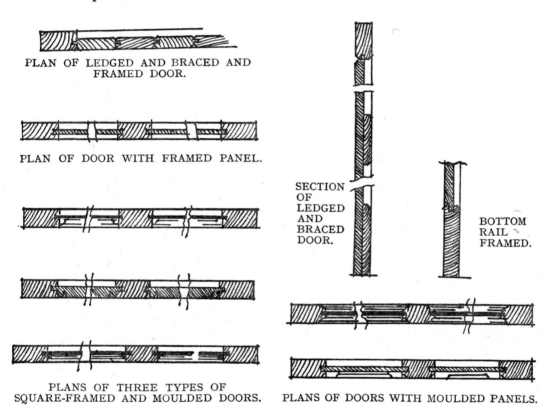

PLAN OF LEDGED AND BRACED AND
FRAMED DOOR.

PLAN OF DOOR WITH FRAMED PANEL.

SECTION
OF
LEDGED
AND
BRACED
DOOR.

BOTTOM
RAIL
FRAMED.

PLANS OF THREE TYPES OF
SQUARE-FRAMED AND MOULDED DOORS.

PLANS OF DOORS WITH MOULDED PANELS.

FIG. 117.

TWICE MOULDED, when both sides are moulded.

BEAD FLUSH, when one side of the panel is flush with the frame, and has a bead worked round the edges to break the joints.

BEAD BUTT, when the bead is worked on the sides of the panel, the end being against the rails.

RAISED PANELS, as the name suggests, have the centre part of the panel thicker than the margin, and are of four varieties :

(1) *Chamfered.*—The panel is chamfered down equally all round from the centre to the edge when squared. When rectangular, the central ridge will be formed.

(2) *Raised and Flat or Chamfered and Filleted.*—In this a chamfer is worked all round the edge, leaving a flat in the centre.

(3) *Raised, Sunk and Chamfered.*—Where the chamfer starts from a marginal sinking below the face.

(4) *Raised, Moulded, Chamfered and Seated.*—When the edge of the sinking is moulded, and a flat is provided for a framed moulding.

STOP CHAMFERED PANELS have the edges of the framing chamfered and steeped in shoulders as shown.

BOLECTION MOULDED PANELS have the moulding raised above the surface and the rails and stiles.

DOUBLE BOLECTION MOULDED have the moulding on each side of the door made in one solid piece, and is grooved to receive the panel, and this is grooved and tongued into the framing.

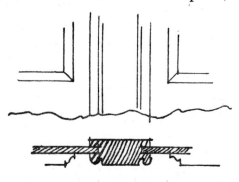

BEADED STYLE
FIG. 122.

DOOR FRAMES AND FINISHINGS

EXTERNAL DOORS.—All frames to external doors and doors in walls where no plaster is used are cut out of the solid and vary from 2″ to $4\frac{1}{2}$″ by 3″ upwards, in accordance with the weight of the door which they carry. The frame itself consists of two side posts and a head. Posts, being termed jambs, are framed into the head with mortise and tenon joints, and the head is generally projected for about 3″ into the brickwork. This projection is termed a horn.

The feet of the jambs or side posts should be dowelled with an iron plug to the stone sill, and where a heavy frame is used a lead pad should be cut to fit the feet of the post. A better method still is to bench up from the stone sill in cement to the underside of the bottom of the post, in order to throw off water which would otherwise lie on the step and rot the feet of the post. In old work and work modelled on old lines, door heads are frequently segmental and sometimes semicircular.

A FLAT SEGMENT is cut out of the solid, while semicircular door heads are built up in several sections, having breaking joints. The posts are connected to the head by means of a hammer-head joint. Where the posts are of a soft nature, it is advisable to fix one or more bent lugs into the jointing of the masonry in the height of the post. It is advisable also to paint the back of the posts where they come against the masonry, and, further, as a protection against damp to inject carbolineum or other wood preservative along the grain of the wood from the feet of the posts. Semicircular headed frames are frequently fitted with a transom light. The jambs of the

Figs. 123, 124.—LEDGED AND BRACED AND LEDGED, BRACED AND FRAMED DOORS.

[C.J.—III.

92]

transom are worked solid, but the head is formed in two thicknesses, glued and screwed together, the one lower being in two lengths and the other in three, so as to break the joint as already described.   Solid frames to entrance doors may have a variety of finishings to the heads. They may be fitted with sashes having fan-shaped tracery, or the heads may be cut into a Tudor arch, in which case the arched portion is some-times made half the width of the frame, to allow for the door being square, the arched portion being framed into the stile, stub mortised and tenoned and pegged with hardwood pegs left to project from the surface, or the whole head may be arched, including the rebate and the door itself framed to fit into the arched portion.

Where it is desired to fold a door back flush, as in a lobby of an office building, for example, it is termed a flush-hung door, and the hinges are fixed on the back of the frame instead of in the usual manner, the other frame being rebated in the usual manner.

INTERNAL DOORS are fitted with jamb linings which are of four varieties : plain, framed, double framed and skeleton framed.

PLAIN LININGS consist of a single board in width, the rebate and stub for the door being formed by nailing a narrower board on the face, thus forming a single rebated plain lining. This form, however, is only met with in cheap work, the better-class work having the same form cut out of the solid. Plain linings are not suitable for walls thicker than 14", in consequence of the amount of surface afforded for shrinkage.

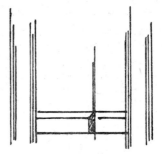

FIG. 125.—CHAMFERED RAIL.

A DOUBLE REBATED PLAIN LINING is cut out of the solid and has a rebate on either side.

In FRAMED LININGS the jambs and soffit are constructed of stiles and rails framed together with mortise and tenon joints, and filled in with panelling which may be moulded or square edged. The panel frames are from $1\frac{1}{2}$" to 2" thick, and are suitable for any opening above 9" thick. The rebates are worked in the solid upon the edges of the stiles, and the frames themselves are put together with mortise and tenon joints stubbed and screwed from the back.

DOUBLE FRAMED LININGS.—As the name suggests, the stiles are made up of two pieces double grooved and tongued, the outer piece being of thicker stuff, fixed securely round the opening, and the inner frame is grooved to it. The tongue should be fitted hand tight but not glued, the object being to fix the rebate frame immovable, to form a good foundation for the architraves and to carry the door.

SKELETON LININGS.—These consist of a frame worked on either side of the wall, having a plain $\frac{1}{2}$" board termed a stub nailed in between.

GROUNDS are required to all openings to form a fixing for the linings and architraves, and should be bevelled or grooved at the back to provide a key for the plaster. They are made out of 1" stuff, the width being governed by the depth of the architrave. They may be regarded as light frames forming a boundary to all openings and plaster work, and they are fixed by nailing to plugs or wood bricks in the walls, and should be square and plumb.

ARCHITRAVES.—The architraves are moulded or panelled finishings fitted to door openings. Running from the door frame to the ground they conceal a joint. When square at the back they are termed single-faced,

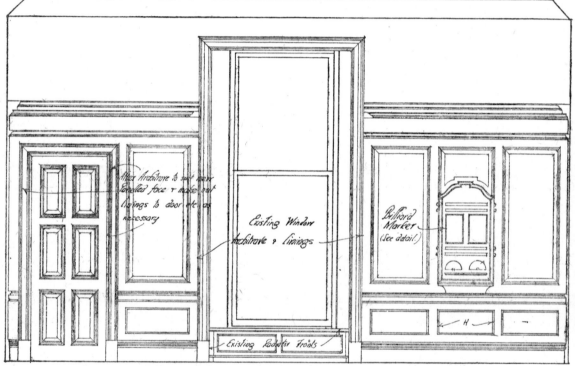

FIG. 126.—INTERIOR DETAIL SHOWING DOUBLE ARCHITRAVES, ETC.
Walter Cave, F.R.I.B.A., Architect.

and Fig. 126 shows a double-faced architrave. It is inadvisable to make architraves wider than 6" in one piece, and very wide architraves may be framed together out of small sections of mouldings. Smaller architraves may have plain mitres at the angle, but with wide architraves the mitres should be grooved and cross-tongued or stub-tenoned and mortised.

Plain blocks at the base of large architraves chamfered from the outside, with face parallel to the line of the moulding, are often fitted at the feet of architraves, being known as *plinth blocks*.

HEAVY ARCHITRAVES are also ploughed and cross-tongued in the mitres, and they are glued and fixed with screws turned in from the back, small under-rail bolts being used to draw the mitres together.

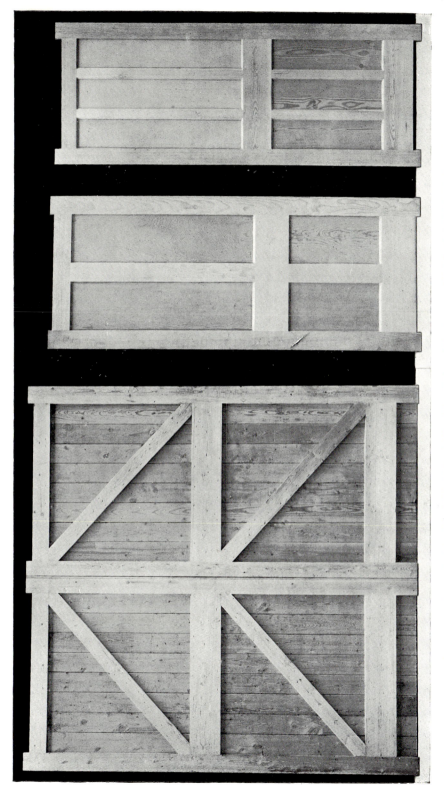

[C.J.—III.

FIGS. 127, 128.—PAIR OF LEDGED AND BRACED AND CHAMFERED PANELLED DOORS.

SLIDING DOORS.—The sliding door as customarily met with in stables, coach-houses, etc., is hung on a track fixed outside the building. The reason for the substitution of this method for the hinged method already described is, of course, the fact that owing to the size and width of the door, not only would the weight be too great for ordinary hinges, but also the space required for the door to swing would be prohibitive. Consequently an overhead track is provided, fixed to the wall above the opening, and on this run grooved wheels or rollers pivoted to brackets which carry the door. In lighter doors the bottom rail is simply grooved to slide smoothly over a runner built into the floor ; but with heavier doors ball-bearing rollers are sunk in the bottom rail. In this method the opening may be closed with one, two or more leaves, according to the width.

SLIDING DOORS IN POCKETS.—External doors, such as front entrance doors, where such a method as that last described would be unsightly, are made to slide into pockets within the walls. As such doors, though narrow, are frequently of heavy construction, they are hung by suspender brackets which carry grooved wheels running over

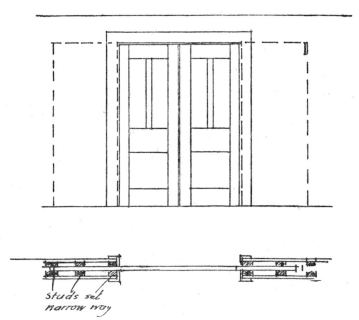

FIG. 129.—INTERIOR SLIDING DOORS.

a knife edge, in a track fixed from side to side of and above the opening. A track is also sunk in the threshold, and over this run rollers let into the bottom rail.

SLIDING DOORS, INTERNAL.—An American practice which has much to commend it when labour saving demands the use of two or more small rooms which can, upon occasion, be made into a large single space, is that of hanging sliding doors between the lounge hall and sitting-room, and sitting-room and dining-room. The practice is rendered easier of accomplishment where stud-framed partitions are used. It is then only necessary to construct the partition in two thicknesses, having the studs placed with their greatest width in the direction of the wall in order to save floor space, the actual width of the hollow depending upon the thickness of the door which is required to slide therein. Conse-

track and hangers being inside are thoroughly protected from the weather. One section swings like an ordinary hinged door, and it is not necessary therefore to open the whole door for gaining entrance to the building when the whole width of opening is not desired for use for the car.

The method of hanging is shown in Fig. 130. It is also suitable for doors in which it is desired to glaze the upper half, each section being made as a separate door and hinged together.

EXTERNAL SLIDING DOORS—PROTECTION AGAINST WEATHER.—Where it is desired to hang sliding doors outside the building for any reason whatever, a weather board may be bracketed to the beam over the opening, in such a manner as to cover the trolley carrying the door. Alternatively the weather board may be fixed to the feet of the rafters, and if required carry a fascia and rain-water gutter. Special double tracks are made for carrying brackets by means of which one door can slide past the other.

SPECIAL DOORS

JIB DOORS.—These are used where it is desired to continue any wall decoration without interruption, and at the same time obtain a door opening. In cases where the walls are plastered, the skirting and frieze rail, if any, is continued across the door, and in panelling the panels are of the same size on the doors and continued regardless of the size of the opening.

FOLDING DOORS.—When an opening is closed by means of two or more flaps, it is termed a folding door. When only two flaps are used, hinged to each frame, it is described as hung folding. In this case the hinges work only one way. Where it is desired to open the door both ways the proper description is hung to swing both ways. Such doors will be found in communicating entrances between kitchens and serveries. To avoid banging, the meeting rails of these doors must be rounded. Where there are several doors, as in screens dividing a large room into several smaller compartments, one door being hinged to the jamb and the other doors being hinged one to the other, they will be found described in specifications, hung folding in so many leaves.

One door only may be used at a time if desired, the others remaining bolted to the floor, or the whole may be folded back against the wall. It will be noted that the greatest weight coming on the hinges on the wall side, these should be larger than the others.

CROSS BATTENED DOORS are used in cottage work for front doors, and as sliding doors for stables and garages. They consist of grooved and tongued battens 5″ by ¾″ nailed or bolted diagonally across and over a framed or framed and braced interior structure. The battens may either cover the whole surface or be rebated into solid stiles and heads. The cross battening acts as a stiffening which, on account of position and exposure in the case of the stable door, is more than usually important.

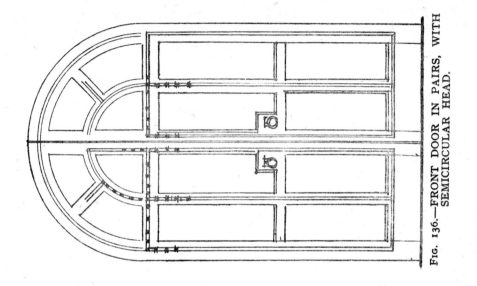

FIG. 136.—FRONT DOOR IN PAIRS, WITH SEMICIRCULAR HEAD.

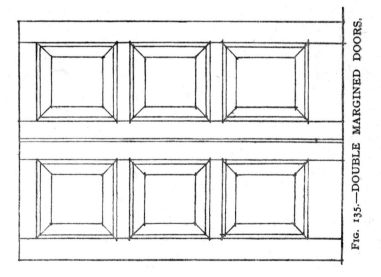

FIG. 135.—DOUBLE MARGINED DOORS.

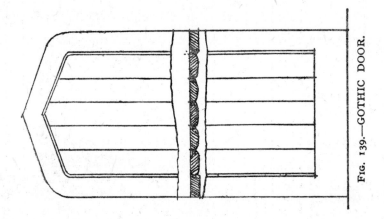

Fig. 139.—GOTHIC DOOR.

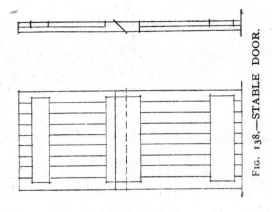

Fig. 138.—STABLE DOOR.

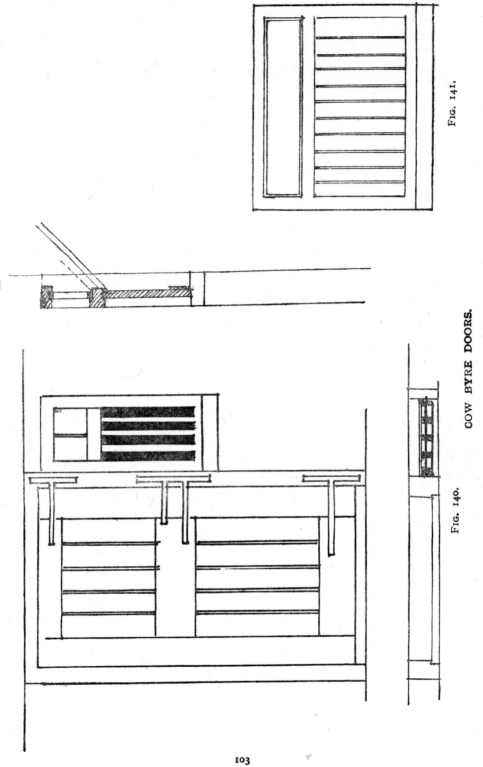

FIG. 141.

FIG. 140.

COW BYRE DOORS.

more even flow and distribution of the moisture-laden air during the process.

Hygrometers are installed in the kilns, permitting a daily reading of the moisture content. The temperature is carefully regulated and recorded by self-registering thermometers. Live steam is used to keep the pores of the wood open and prevent case hardening, and speed is also a consideration, for if the modern requirements in quantity are to be met, there is no unnecessary time to be lost. The proper condition of the wood, however, is not to be sacrificed to speed. It would be interesting to note, while on this subject of dry-kilns, that in modern plants the lumber is piled on the kiln trucks entirely by machinery, each truck containing a given quantity of a given thickness and width automatically segregated and distributed.

Proper treatment requires that the wood, after leaving the kiln, be kept for a number of days in a conditioning room, before going to the planers and cutting rooms for final cutting into proper dimensions for stiles and rails.

A further important step in the evolution of the modern door is the development of the ply-wood for panels. However carefully wood may be treated, it is impossible to be sure that material of the proper thickness and width for the wide panels of modern design will stand the vagaries of the British climate. Strength, coupled with security against warping or checking, requires a built-up panel, and this panel must be built up with a cement between its plies which will withstand moisture under all conditions. The development of the ply-wood industry in the past two decades was in response to this demand. The result is, manufactured timber of any reasonably required width much stronger than solid wood of equal thickness and free from the old bugbears of checking and warping.

This principle has been carried into the construction of stiles and rails. Solid stiles *will* sometimes twist in spite of every care in selection and treatment. " Nature unaided fails "—a maxim which is familiar to students of such things. Little by little this thought took root and grew until its fruition in the built-up or " Laminex " doors.

The name Laminex has been coined by common usage to indicate a process of laminated or building up with layers of wood with the direction of the grain crossing alternately at right angles. In this process the stiles and rails are built up of small pieces dovetailed and glued together. The theory was that the strain or tendency to warp in one piece will be counteracted by its neighbour piece, a theory which holds good in practice. These small bits are assembled, dovetailed and glued to the required width and length for stiles and rails, and the whole covered with a sheet of veneer of the same wood and subjected to enormous pressure, thus forcing the component parts into one solid mass, the waterproof cement permeating the adjacent parts to make a solid and impermeable whole.

It is not necessary to sacrifice considerations of good taste in the

Fig. 142.—STABLE DOOR, BACK AND FRONT.

modern manufacture of doors, in fact this built-up process lends itself the more readily to the consideration of beauty in architecture, for the reason that stiles and particularly bottom and lock rails can be made of suitable width to satisfy the demands of good proportions, while the three-ply panels can be made as wide and long as is required for any type of door that may be required. Indeed, this process has made possible the so-called flush or hospital door without panels, resembling a solid piece of lumber in width, height and thickness without blemish.

Standardised doors have long been made of various woods depending upon locality. For many years pine was the favourite for low-priced doors, but the old-fashioned soft almost grainless pine has long since become classed among the rare and costly woods. The vast forests of what is known as Columbian Pine, which stands in such unbroken stretches in the Canadian North-West and in the north-western parts of the United States, have in recent years supplied an increasing part of the world's requirements for a suitable door timber for doors of low and medium cost. Standardised doors are also made even of mahogany, the built-up process permitting the use of a cheaper wood for the cores or built-up parts, while a smaller amount is used for the outside for exposed parts.

Doors, as described above, have been brought to England in vast quantities by the Woco Door Company, Dashwood House, London, and Cunard Buildings, Liverpool.

A BUTTERFLY DOOR is hung to revolve by means of pivots at the centre in the top and bottom rails, Fig. 153.

HOSPITAL DOORS.—For use in hospitals, where it is desired to offer as little lodgment for dust as possible, special doors are designed having a plain surface throughout. The American method involves the construction of a pine core, as described under, and the facing thereof with a hardwood veneer.

This method, however, has been superseded by plywood surfacings formed over a hollow frame. The framework consists of light styles and rails with cross braces and stiffeners. This type has the advantage of being cheaper than the solid door, and the air space should provide a good sound deadener.

PLYWOOD FLAT SURFACE DOORS, although first introduced for use in hospitals, infirmaries and schools, are now finding favour for decorative reasons. Flat doors of this kind provide a fine surface for painting, which is considered an advantage in some decorative schemes, but more often the aim is to display the beauty of the natural wood colouring and veining, the plywood veneers being merely varnished or polished. In this way it is possible to obtain a continuity of effect with the other woodwork, possibly wainscoting, of the room. While the surface of the door is kept perfectly flat, it is easy to secure very beautiful results by quartering the veneers or following other methods to produce striking patterns from the highly figured timbers. On the other hand, as explained in another chapter of this book, with veneered plywood a continuous length and breadth of wood can be obtained, showing off the figuring and veining of the wood to perfection. Whichever method is chosen there is a decorative gain. The chief difficulty in finishing off finely veneered plywood is in dealing with the edges, which are apt to fray, particularly with certain brittle woods. One way of overcoming this is to cause the outer framework of the door to project slightly all round, and house the plywood sheet within the beading, which is then planed down to the general surface. A sound method is to make the door $\frac{1}{4}$" smaller all round than the framing of the doorway, and then glue on a covering strip $\frac{1}{4}$" thick, bridging frame and veneer, finishing off flat. A third method, only applicable where a slight projection is not objected to, is to fasten a covering strip, usually 1" to 3" broad, and not more than $\frac{1}{4}$" thick, all round the door, using a hard, tough wood to protect the edges.

Doors of this type are light but very strong. Locks and hinges must, of course, be fastened to the solid framing.

WOOD FINISHINGS TO ROOMS

In addition to the architraves fixed around door and window openings already described, it is customary in all rooms to fix a wooden skirting to cover the joint of the floor boards and the walls, and also to serve as a stop to the legs of furniture, thus to protect the plaster surface of the wall from being damaged by the too close approach of corners of heavy articles of furniture.

Skirtings vary from 3" to 15" in height, a plain skirting consisting of only a single beam having its upper face chamfered or moulded as desired. Built-up skirtings consist of two or more pieces tongued together, each piece being moulded separately, the whole then put together forming one continuous moulding. The skirtings are fixed to the walls by means of firring, and plastered between grounds, which are narrow strips of wood of the same thickness as the plaster; the upper one is placed about $\frac{1}{2}$" below the top of the skirting, being bevelled inwards on its outer surface to give fixing for the plaster.

The lower one is known as a fillet and is fixed along the floor on top of the floor boards. The firrings or pluggings are short upright pieces from 2' 6" to 4' 0" apart placed vertical between the grounds. Wood blocks are driven into the wall between the joints of the brickwork for nailing the grounds to, or fixing bricks made of coke breeze and cement are built in for that purpose.

The joint between the skirting and the floor may be merely fitted close down on to it, when it is described as being *scribed* ; but a better method is by means of a groove and tongue joint. Alternatively the angle may be filled in by a bead moulding or cavetto if desired. The external angles of skirtings are mitred and cross-bradded or mitred and

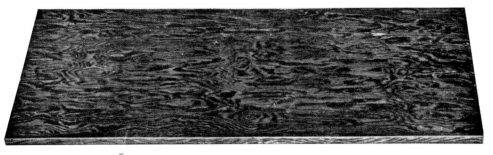

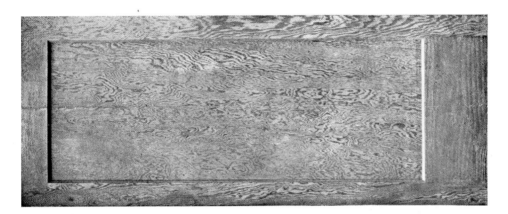

FIGS. 143, 144, 145.—PATENT COMPOSITE DOORS. HOSPITAL DOOR.

[C.J.—III.

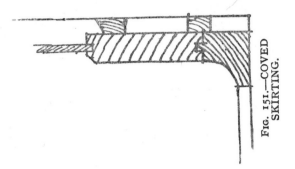

Fig. 151.—COVED
SKIRTING.

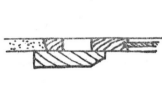
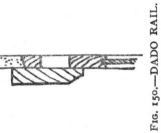

Fig. 150.—DADO RAIL.

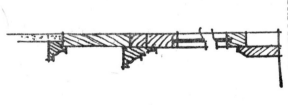

Fig. 149.—PANELLING.

dovetailed, and the internal angles have the square portion tongued and grooved and the mouldings scribed.

For the fixing of built-up skirtings, blocks are inserted where hardwood or polished finishings are desired, nails or screw fixings are concealed in the manner known as *secret fixing*. This consists of screws driven into the grounds or backings, with the heads left projecting $\frac{1}{2}''$ to $\frac{3}{8}''$, slits being formed in the back of the skirting to receive them or small dovetail pieces of hardwood being secured to the ground and corresponding dovetail mortises made in the skirting.

DADOS.—The simplest form of dado consists of matched lining with a plain chamfered or moulded capping. More expensive and ornate forms, known as framed dados, consist of moulded and sometimes carved panelling. A *dado rail* is sometimes fitted at a height of 3' 6" to protect the wall from the backs of chairs placed against it, the boarding or panelling being omitted. Where the dado is fixed, the skirting is sometimes placed on the face of it, or in the case of panelled dados the skirting forms the bottom member. The framing of *framed dados* is fitted together by means of mortised and tenoned joints, mouldings where possible being worked in the solid and mitred round the panels. The external angles in dado framing should be dovetail mitred, and the internal angles tongued and grooved and the capping mitred. The capping consists of a top mould having a cover mould tenoned into it, behind which the top rail of the panelling is held. Framed dados are secured to the walls by framed grounds in such a manner that a backing is provided to all the principal parts of the dado frame. These grounds should be constructed out of not less than 1" stuff and framed together by means of the mortise and tenon joint. After the grounds are in place, the spaces in between are filled in with one or two coats of " rough stuff," but the plaster must be perfectly dry before the dado is fixed.

PANELLING is more truly applicable in description of wall coverings in wood which extend over the whole or greater part of the wall. The construction is similar to that of a dado.

PICTURE RAILS are mouldings or chamfered strips run round the room at a convenient height for the hanging of pictures and form an artistic finish when made to line with the top member of the architrave over the door head. They are moulded in such a way that the top member projects sufficiently to carry a picture hook.

FRIEZES are sometimes made of wood being the portion of the wall which occurs immediately below the cornice and where this is the case the cornice itself is generally framed in wood also. When made of wood, friezes are not as a rule framed, but usually consist of boarding laid horizontally and fixed by means of a grooved and tongued joint to the picture rail along the lower edge, and by a similar joint at the top to the bottom member of the cornice. When over 6" in width, a frieze should be made up of two or more pieces grooved and tongued together and dovetail keyed at the back to prevent casting. Friezes are often

FIGS. 146, 147, 148.—PATENT COMPOSITE DOORS.

richly carved and decorated, and when this is the case upright wood backings are provided for securing to the wall, and should be placed from 2' 6" to 4' 0" apart.

WOOD CORNICES are formed by building up rectangular pieces of wood grooved and tongued together, moulded and shaped on the outside in such a manner that the various parts compose the whole moulding of the cornice. The mitreing of a built-up cornice must be executed with care in order to obtain a well-fitting joint throughout the entire depth. All angles of built-up cornices should be mitred and dowelled.

CEILINGS.—Where cornices are in wood, the ceilings are also frequently panelled out in wood to various designs. The simplest form of wood-covered ceilings consists of matched boarding nailed to the underside of the joists, or it may be arranged to pattern, having a moulding planted on the face to form imitation panels. This moulding must be arranged so as to cover all the heading joints under the boarding. Framing and panelling constructed in the same way as for walls is also fixed directly to the joists, a small cover moulding being planted on over the screws by which the framing is secured to the joists. The panels in wooden ceilings should not be fitted tightly into the grooves in framing, but should be given room to shrink or swell without splitting. They should be arranged in convenient sizes in order to avoid jointing as much as possible ; and where jointing is necessary, they must be grooved, tongued and glued, and have keys fixed across the grain at the back by means of screws in brass slots.

In a ceiling, however, it is much better to have a number of small panels than a few large ones, owing to the fact that the hot air rising subjects the woodwork in this position to more varying temperatures than in any other.

DATA

	Height.	Breadth.	Thickness.
Entrance doors . . .	7' 0" to 8' 6"	3' 0" to 4' 6"	2" to 3"
Reception rooms . .	7' 0"	3' 3"	2"
Bedroom . . .	6' 8"	2' 8"	1½"

Styles and top rails out of 4½".
Frieze rails 4".
Middle and bottom rails 9".
Height of lock rail 2' 8" to centre.

MATERIALS :
    Common doors are made of yellow deal.
    Interior common doors, yellow deal frames and American white panels.
    Better-class doors are made of Honduras mahogany, black walnut and oak. Pine and baywood veneered with Spanish mahogany.
    External doors of walnut, yellow pine, cedar, pitch pine, teak and oak.

CHAPTER V

FITTINGS

DOMESTIC FITTINGS

IF a comparison were to be made between the domestic conditions of the Victorian era and present times, it would be rather of the nature of a contrast. Consequently building, especially house building, being the architectural expression of the social conditions and desires of the times, it is but natural to expect that our buildings will alter in sympathy with any change in those conditions. And it would be equally true of the Victorian age to describe it as one of prosperity and pride in house property, as it would to describe the present as a time when house property has become for a time, whilst still a necessity, an incumbrance in which economy of every sort is of the first importance.

In the Victorian age domestic service was regarded as an occupation worthy of real effort and care, whilst for a period following it became to be regarded with disfavour and as an occupation of a temporary nature, only to be engaged in all others failing.

Many causes contributed to this swinging of the pendulum from one extreme to the other, amongst which were, no doubt, the social upheaval, the growth of cheap restaurants, tea-shops and large departmental stores, replacing coffee-houses, inns and shops in which the staff was confined to the proprietor's family. These new developments offered occupations thought to be less restricted and to offer more openings to persons who till that time had entered domestic service as a natural course. Consequently, human nature being what it is, it was perhaps only natural that a plentiful supply of domestic servants led to a disregard of their comfort. And, as a consequence, the serviceability of the offices in which they worked was not given very much consideration. Equally natural

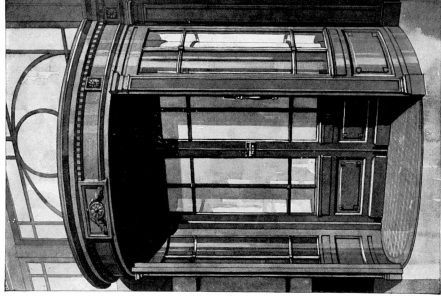

FIG. 153.—BUTTERFLY DOOR.

[C.J.—III.

FIG. 152.—GLAZED FRONT DOOR.

to human nature is it, when the major part of the domestic work fell upon the residents of the house, that consideration should be given to the reduction of that work and any means of saving labour should be eagerly sought.

Where in the past architects at the will of their clients had given expression to this sense of pride in property, they later turned their attention to economy of construction and domestic labour. And, as in all things the happy mean lies between extremes, it may well be that with the increased facility of working a house and in the improvement of the condition of the domestic offices and servants' bedrooms as habitable rooms, there will follow a return of that regard for domestic service as a pleasant and comfortable occupation.

If this is so, it would be no exaggeration to say that building owners and architects have a duty to the community which may not be lightly regarded. This lies in a very careful study of the planning of a house in such a manner as to save all unnecessary labour. In England it is true that we are conservative and dislike all change, but this national characteristic should not be allowed to interfere with, and by no means prevent, the amelioration of our internal domestic circumstances. For it cannot be too clearly realised that the solution to the domestic service problem lies in the first place, if not entirely, in the planning of the home.

THE PASS PANTRY

In no better way is this point exemplified than in consideration of the relation of the kitchen to the dining-room and the spaces intervening between the one and the other and the consequent carrying of loads and walking necessitated.

A study of the planning in this respect will give the keynote of the whole tendency. If, for example, the plan of Hatfield House be compared with that of any large residence typical of those being built to-day in the United States, America, the effect of domestic conditions will be at once evident.

As has been said, the deciding factor in the lay-out of the plan is the plentifulness or scarcity of domestic servants. There is also, of course, tradition and history to be taken into account with the mediæval residence. In the castle the dining-hall having somewhat of a public character, any traveller in the neighbourhood being admitted to the one meal of the day, it was perhaps only to be expected that, in times when social distinctions counted for so much more than they do to-day, the feast should be made the occasion of much ceremony, which, besides adding prestige to the noble and his family, also had a disciplinary effect upon those chance guests in a day when table manners had not reached that state of refinement which obtains to-day.

Then processions of cooks and their staff from kitchens to dining-hall were ceremonies well calculated to impress all who were admitted and

passage or back verandah, in the manner shown in the accompanying diagram.

PANTRY FITTINGS

Where the matter is decided in some such manner as that suggested, the deciding factor in the fittings required in the pass pantry, with, as always, the desire to save time and unnecessary walking and carrying, will be that the china, glass and cutlery used in the dining-room should be stored in the pantry, the operation of washing-up should take place there, and these articles should leave the pantry only at such times as when they are in use for a meal.

This provision will be found of especial benefit in such houses where one maid only is kept. The maid will probably do most of the cooking, whilst the house-maid's duties will be under-taken by one or more of the members of the family ; and in such circumstances a separate sink and store cupboard will be appreciated.

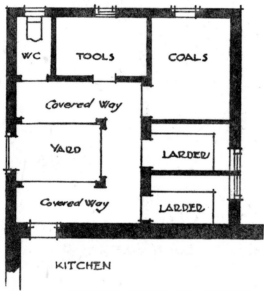

FIG. 156.—COVERED YARD AND OFFICES.

The first requisite will be the sink, which may be of copper where funds permit, or, failing that, of teak. It should be placed on an outer wall directly under a window, the sill of which is kept at a height sufficient to allow convenient space for the hot and cold taps over the sink. Where, as is only too frequently seen, this point is overlooked, and the window-sill built at such a height that the window board comes only just above the top of the sink and level with the draining-board, considerable inconvenience is occasioned. The pipes and taps having, by such a method, no solid ground for fixing, necessitate the introduction of strips of horizontal boarding fixed to an upright. This is a practice which can be described by no other term than " botching," and one which defeats in part the purpose of the window, which is to admit light and ventilation. It is also one which renders the window difficult to open, and at the same time, by reason of the uprights and cross pieces, gives additional surfaces and corners for the collection of grease and dirt, difficult to be got at.

THE PANTRY SINK

The sink where formed of teak should be fitted with a cover of $1\frac{1}{4}''$

FIG. 154.—MODERN INTERIOR FINISH IN WOODWORK.

mortise and mitre-clamped flap with rounded nosing, and hung with 3″ brass butts to beaded frame to lift up. The space underneath may be enclosed with 1¼″ beaded frame and square-framed doors, hung with 3″ brass butts and fitted with two 3″ brass barrel bolts and brass knob turn-buckle. Behind and above the sink, a finish may be given by fixing a 9″ by 1″ ovolo moulded skirting—or, if preferred, the space between top of sink and underside of window board may be tiled in squares, or, for economy, plastered in Keenes Cement, lined in squares and painted.

When the sink is lined with lead, an 8-lb. lead should be used, the edges turned over, closely copper nailed and bedded in white lead. A 2″

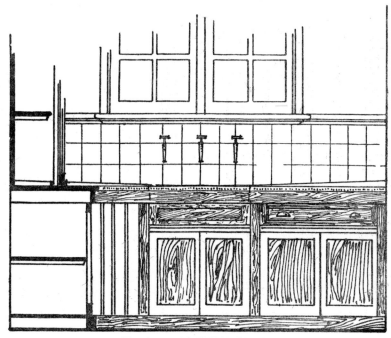

FIG. 157.—PANTRY SINK.

pantry washer plug and brass chain, 2″ trap with brass cap and screw, and 2″ lead waste to deliver into the gulley outside the wall, must be included.

The draining-board may be covered with pewter, 3½ lb. per foot superficial, carefully dressed into the flutes and over the edges.

If lined with copper, tinned copper, 3¼ lb. per foot superficial, should be carefully dressed over the top edges and braced at the joints.

WOOD SINK DETAILS

SINK FITTINGS.—A 2″ top should be fixed at 3′ 0″ from the floor, perforated to fit over the top of the sink, the edges of the opening being

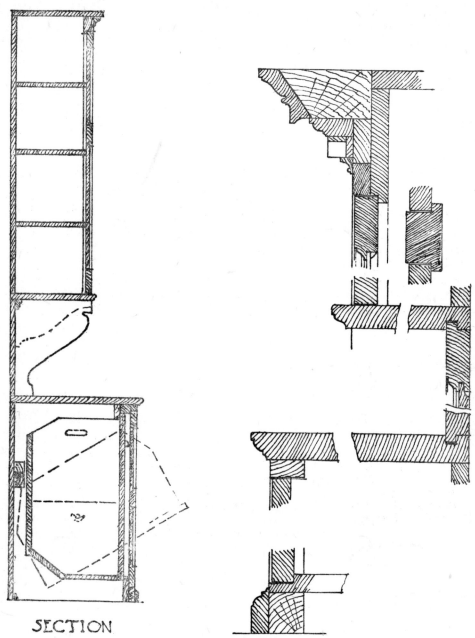

SECTION

FIG. 163.—KITCHEN AND PANTRY DRESSER DETAILS.

and blocked. On the rims are screwed $\frac{3}{4}''$ by $2''$ deal runners. Underneath the drawers there is fitted a $1''$ pot board on bearers. The ends are enclosed with $1\frac{1}{4}''$ square framing and the front with $1''$ framed and beaded with $1\frac{1}{4}''$ square-framed doors hung folded. In the cupboard a $1''$ shelf with $1''$ divisions is fitted. The back of the dresser is formed of $\frac{3}{4}''$ matched and beaded boarding in $4''$ widths.

KITCHENETTE

In many modern houses, especially those provided with a general living-room, and again in town flats, comparatively little room is given

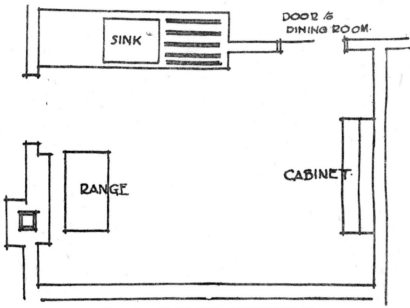

FIG. 164.—PLAN FOR KITCHENETTE.

up to the kitchen, and we then have the kitchenette. In such cases it is necessary to make the very best use of the space available, and then the skill of the joiner is particularly in request. The fittings described in the preceding and succeeding pages will show how his skill can be brought to bear on the problem, and the accompanying plan will help in the placing of the fittings.

KITCHEN CUPBOARD

Where the form of dresser fully described above is used, an additional closed-in cupboard will be required in the kitchen. This should be placed in a convenient position in which its projection will not cause inconvenience, preferably in a recess, and should extend from floor to ceiling and have a 1½″ framed and beaded front in two heights. The lower part should be fitted with 1½″ square-framed doors, hung folding with 3″ iron butts. Also similar doors should be fitted to the upper part. The top should be finished with 3″ by 2″ moulding as cornice, and four 1¼″ wrought both sides shelves, with chamfered bearer, should be fitted.

MODERN KITCHEN CABINETS

Labour-saving methods have introduced in place of the dresser last mentioned cadinets which, being movable fitments, may be regarded as furniture.

The principle underlying the furnishing of the modern kitchen is that, as nearly as may be possible, all energy wasted in walking may be saved, and every article in use so handily placed that the major portion of the work may be done from a stool. To this end the modern kitchen is of small dimensions, and all the requisites for cooking a meal, and also the sink for washing-up, and the gas-stove or " Kooksjoie " Stove, handily placed to both.

The cabinet consists of a table top at a height of from 3′ 0″ to 3′ 3″ from the floor, with panelled sides and pedestals of three drawers on either side with one drawer in the middle over a space to accommodate the knees and feet of the person using the cabinet when seated on a stool. Above, plain shelving is fitted, the two top shelves being closed in with doors having either wood or glass panels. The lower shelf is open at a height convenient for the accommodation of canisters about 18″ above the table top, which extends to the back of the cabinet.

THE SINK.—In a convenient recess the sink is situated, being an enamelled metal or stoneware sink, in a teak surround, and having a draining-board at a proper angle.

The draining-board may be made of additional convenience and comfort in the following manner. At its lower edge, i.e. that at the edge of the sink, it is hinged so that when the sink is not in use it may be folded over the sink to shut it out from view, and, if desired, a table-cloth may be spread over the whole. When opened for use, the draining-board folds back, resting on a bearer at a height requisite to give the board a satisfactory slope down towards the sink. And as the labour of washing-up is greatly increased by the fact that on the old-fashioned draining-board an insufficient drainage is provided whereby considerable water accumulates, in this instance the angle of the draining-board is such that any accumulation is prevented. But the angle being steep, some method of preventing the crockery from sliding is necessary. So that for the accommodation of the cups a double row of wood pins is supplied, over which the cups may be inverted to drain. Next there are

FIG. 162.—BOOKCASE WITH DRAWERS.

FIG. 161.—WARDROBE WITH SLIDING TRAYS AND
DRAWERS.

V-shaped grooves cut in the board at right angles to the half-round drainage grooves, each having above it a rail against which the saucers and small plates may be rested, their bottom edge being held by the V-shaped groove. A similar rail on taller pegs and another V-shaped groove above this provides for the larger plates ; whilst mushroom-topped pegs above this second rail afford facility for the larger dishes and pots. It will be found that if really hot water is used in washing-up, utensils drained in this manner will be almost dry by the time the washing-up is finished, leaving little to be done in the way of drying but mere polishing.

Directly above the sink, at a **convenient** height, there are two shelves for china, and above this again a shelf for pots and pans.

If the stove, either a gas-stove or some form which burns anthracite, such as a " Kooksjoie," be placed conveniently handy to the cabinet, a very considerable amount of energy spent in walking from and round the different heavy articles in an old-fashioned kitchen will be saved.

Another form of cabinet, known as a kitchenette, has as a basic principle that when closed up nothing of its interior purpose appears. The lower portion consists of a pedestal of four drawers on the right hand and two cupboard doors on the left hand, providing space for the accommodation of pots and pans, the lids being slipped in behind wood rails on the inner face of the doors. Above this lower portion is a sliding top having a slab, which can be pulled out when required for pastry making, and slid back out of view when the cabinet is closed. The back of the upper portion is fitted centrally with a fresh-water filter, to which the water main is connected, and on either hand are three rows of shelving. Hinged to the outer edge of this upper portion are box-shaped or circular-shaped doors, each of which has three rows of narrow shelves, with rails providing recesses suitable for small articles, such as cocoa, mustard and other tins, sauce bottles, etc.

The cabinet is made of three-ply wood, finished mahogany, and when closed presents a pleasing appearance. The shelves and glass top are removable for cleaning, and the drawers fitted as flour bins, cake drawer and bread locker are lined with tin, soldered at the joints and fitted with air-tight hinged lids to lift up. The whole when closed has the following dimensions : height 5' 6", width 4' 4", depth at top 15", depth at bottom 2' 8".

By the adoption of such devices in planning a small kitchen, not only is considerable labour saved in the kitchen, and also cost in building unnecessary kitchen floor area, but also two other rooms are rendered unnecessary. Both the scullery and the pantry will be no longer required when this composite kitchenette is installed. This, in a time when every possible economy must be adopted in planning, will be found to be of very vital importance.

VARIOUS DETAILS

MODIFIED CABINET.—Another form of kitchen cabinet, combining the pantry fitting and American type of dresser, consists of two parts, an upper and a lower. The upper portion has two outer cupboards fitted with shelves, the bottom part of one having a tilting flour bin as described in the American dresser. In between the shelf above this and the next full-depth shelf is a narrow one for small articles.

The pedestal has at its right-hand side a stack of four short drawers, and two-thirds of its width on the left-hand side is given up to a long drawer for table-cloths, having a double-fronted cupboard under that on the left, being fitted with shelves, and a sliding grid upon which pots from the stove can be stood. Lid racks, as previously described, are fitted on the inside of the doors. The upper and lower parts are made separate and screwed together. And the table top between them is constructed to slide out to form a wider work table. It is clamped, and has its edges tipped and slides on a hardwood strip let into the edge of the top.

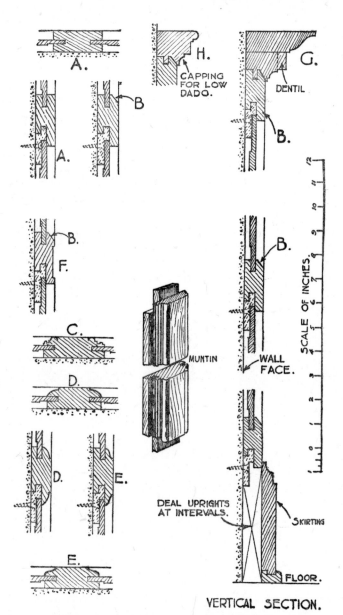

FIG. 165.—DETAILS OF PANELLING.

SCULLERY SINKS AND FITTINGS.—The old-fashioned scullery is provided with an earthenware sink with teak or deal wood surround, and 1½″ draining-board cut with rounded grooves ¾″ wide, ½″ deep and 1″ apart blocked up to fall. Underneath the sink, which is carried either on brickwork piers or metal brackets, a cupboard front is fixed, with hinged doors hung therein, and shelves on wood bearers. Above the sink, or at the side, plate-racks are plugged to the walls.

BUTLER'S CUPBOARD. — Either in conjunction with the scullery sink, or in the pantry if provided, a fitting for the reception of the china and glass should be provided, such as is shown in Fig. 158. This consists of a pedestal fitted with two stacks of drawers, and a cupboard above fitted with shelves and enclosed with glazed doors. The doors may either be hinged at the outsides with the central one made to slide either way, or all three may be made to slide in between fillets fixed as guides and upon hardwood runners. The runner is let into the top and bottom of the upper cupboard, and works easily in a groove cut in the top and bottom rail of the glazed door or sash. The sides of the upper portion are made of 1¼″ stuff beaded on the inner face angle, and the upper portion

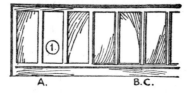

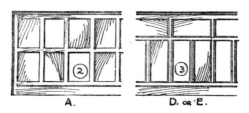

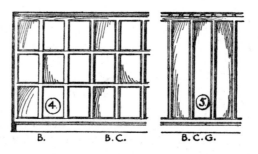

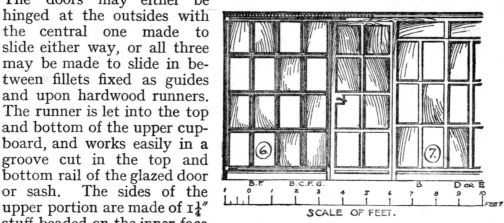

FIG. 166.—TYPES OF PANELLING.

has a depth of 10″ from the outside of the back to the outside of the door, and a height of 4′ 6″ from bottom to top. The top and bottom of the cupboard should be dovetailed at the sides and the dovetails concealed. The back is made of matched lining,

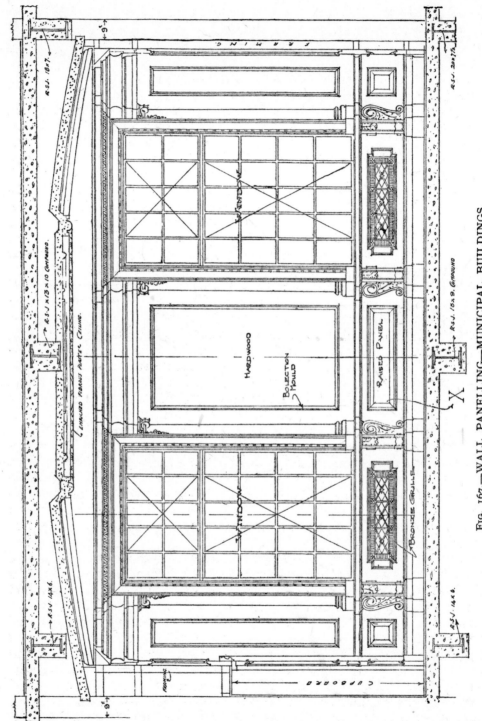

FIG. 167.—WALL PANELLING—MUNICIPAL BUILDINGS.

E. C. P. Monson, F.R.I.B.A, F.S.I., Architect.

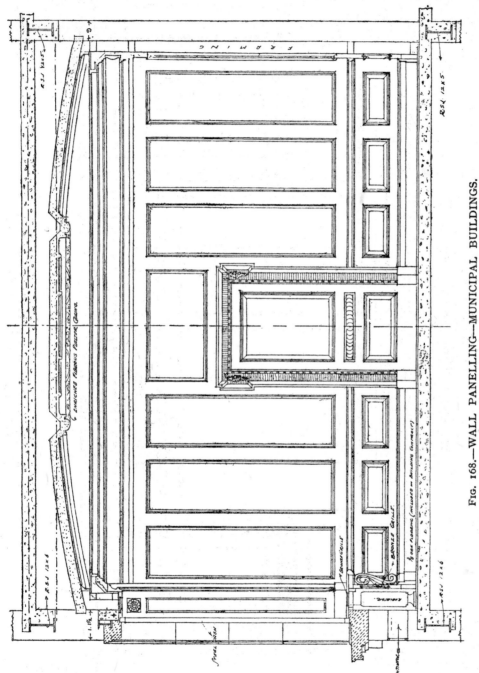

FIG. 168.—WALL PANELLING—MUNICIPAL BUILDINGS.
E. C. P. Monson, F.R.I.B.A., F.S.I., Architect.

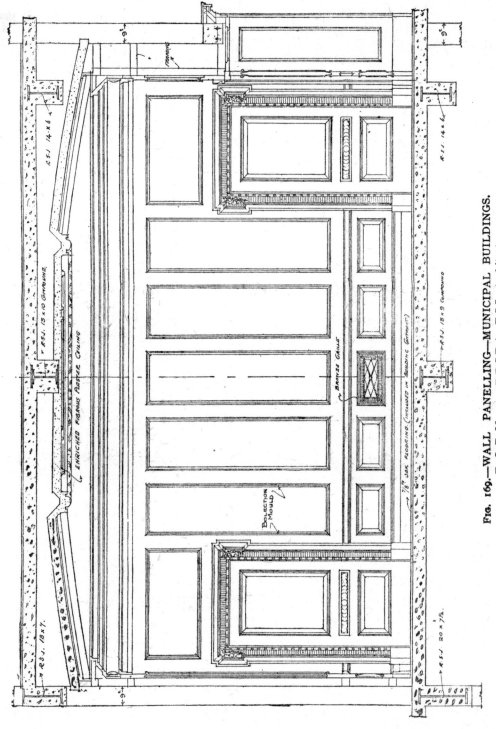

FIG. 169.—WALL PANELLING—MUNICIPAL BUILDINGS.
E. C. P. Monson, F.R.I.B.A., F.S.I., Architect.

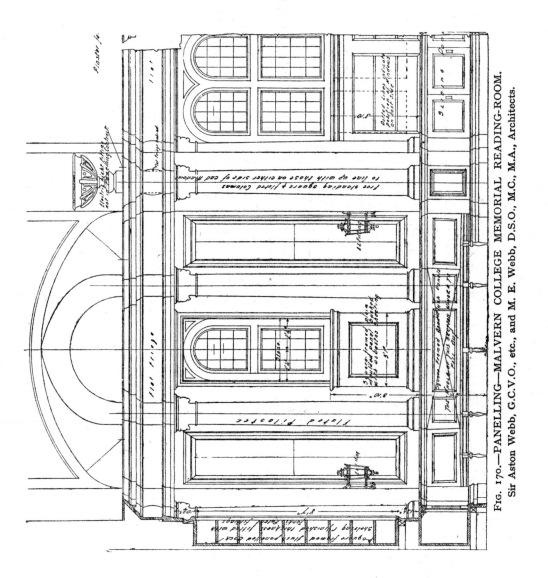

FIG. 170.—PANELLING—MALVERN COLLEGE MEMORIAL READING-ROOM.
Sir Aston Webb, G.C.V.O., etc., and M. E. Webb, D.S.O., M.C., M.A., Architects.

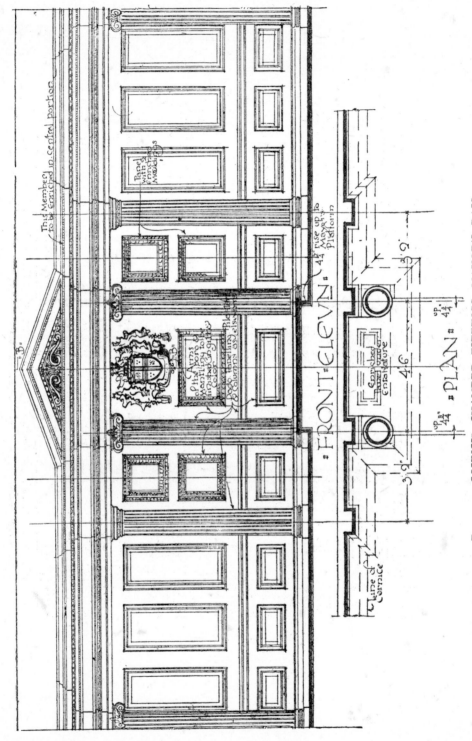

FRONT ELEVN.

PLAN.

FIG. 171.—COUNCIL CHAMBER FITTINGS—MAYOR'S DAIS.
E. C. P. Monson, F.R.I.B.A., F.S.I., Architect.

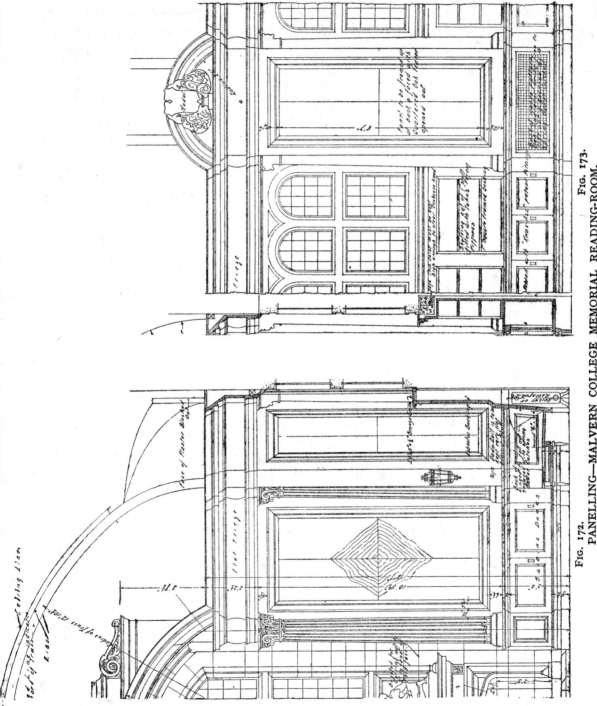

FIG. 172.

FIG. 173.

PANELLING—MALVERN COLLEGE MEMORIAL READING-ROOM.

Sir Aston Webb, G.C.V.O., etc., and M. E. Webb, D.S.O., M.C., M.A., Architects.

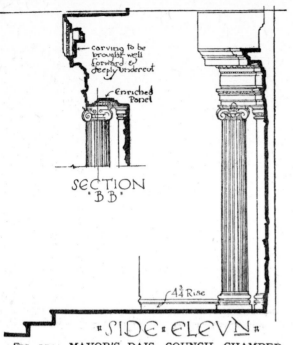

carving to be
brought well
forward &
deeply undercut

Enriched
Panel

SECTION
"BB"

4¾ Rise

SIDE ELEVN

FIG. 174.—MAYOR'S DAIS—COUNCIL CHAMBER
FITTINGS.

E. C. P. Monson, F.R.I.B.A., F.S.I., Architect.

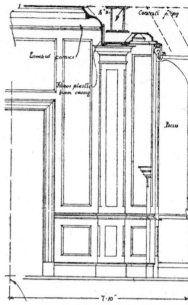

Enriched cornice

Fibrous plaster
beam casing

Beam

Beam

7'.10"

FIG. 175.—SECTION THROUGH
FIREPLACE RECESS.

Walter Cave, F.R.I.B.A., Architect.

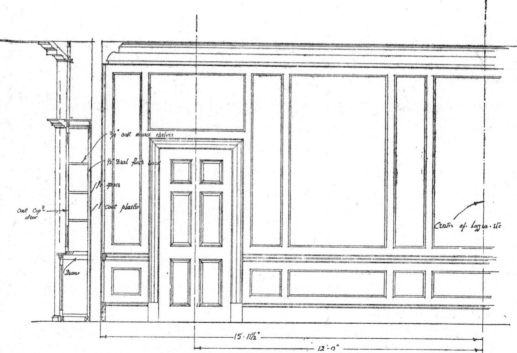

Centre of Loggia. Etc.

15'.11½"

12'.0"

FIG. 176.—LIBRARY PANELLING.

Walter Cave, F.R.I.B.A., Architect.

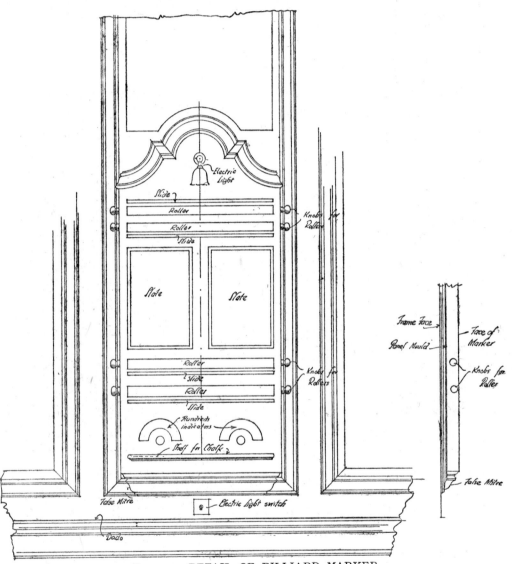

FIG. 177.—DETAIL OF BILLIARD MARKER.
Walter Cave, F.R.I.B.A., Architect.

FIG. 178.—PANELLING—MALVERN COLLEGE MEMORIAL READING-ROOM.
Sir Aston Webb, G.C.V.O., etc., and M. E. Webb, D.S.O., M.C., M.A., Architects.

the top $\frac{1}{2}''$ being left to show and forming the top member of the skirting.

At door and window openings the wainscoting is finished against the architrave, which should be of sufficient depth to take the greatest projection of any moulding forming part of the wainscoting. Alternatively a pilaster may be introduced between the architrave and wainscoting to finish the wainscoting against.

A useful capping to wainscoting in kitchens, and decorative also where the kitchen is used as a living-room, is one in which the capping becomes a narrow bracketed shelf, $3\frac{3}{4}''$ by $\frac{3}{4}''$, or where less projection is desired, the shelf is then $1\frac{1}{8}''$ by $3''$, and in both cases nailed to a ground fixed to the brickwork. Such a shelf will be found convenient and decorative for the accommodation of brass trays or china in frequent use.

STORE CLOSETS

A better plan than the store fitting of cupboard fronts and shelving in the kitchen is the provision of separate chambers or closets for the accommodation of house-keeper's stores. In this case all that is required is several rows of $1\frac{1}{4}''$ wrought both sides shelves, supported by chamfered wood bearers and stout gibbeted brackets. Also, unless a window is possible in an outside wall, some form of ventilation should be provided, either by means of a louvre vent over the door in place of a transom light, or in the form of a grating in one or more panels of the door. The louvres are let into chases cut diagonally in the frame for their reception. The frame is continued up and formed as in the case of a glazed transom light. When panels are pierced for ventilation, these may be either simply holes bored in them with a brace and bit, or shaped patterns cut out with a keyholer's fret-saw, or the wood panel replaced with a perforated zinc or copper gauze screen. Whatever the nature of the opening, it is advisable to cover it by means of a fly-proof covering as mentioned, fixing the covering on the inside of the door by a frame of narrow strips rebated at the angles and sprigged to the door panels or stiles and rails to hold the edges of the screen.

LINEN CLOSETS.—It is found convenient to frame off a portion of the bathroom to house the hot-water cylinder, and this provides a convenient place for the linen closet. But it is worthy of note that wherever possible the door to the closet should not open into the bathroom, on account of the steam.

Where the cupboard is formed by lath and plaster partitions on three sides, nothing more is required than a cupboard front with doors and shelves composed of $\frac{1}{2}''$ battens resting on $1\frac{1}{2}''$ bearers at their ends.

Where the fitment is framed in wood entirely, it has a matched back and sides, and front framed and panelled, or the sides may be simply matched like the back. At the angle where the back and front join, a rounded corner post is inserted, beaded on its inner edge and rebated to receive the door. At a height of 2' 6" there is a cross rail rebated to

could be used. Then, again, the glass lining can be omitted from the lower sections of the cupboards, and wooden panelled doors in place of glazed ones adopted ; for instance, when such lower sections are fitted as a coal or log store, or a cellarette, or otherwise. When the recess is not deep, as with present-day chimney breasts, narrow shelves, shaped to the walls, mitred at the angles, or tongued and grooved on the square, or with circular outer sweep (bowed or semi-lunar), can be used, and the glazed doors dispensed with altogether. Such details, however, will depend largely upon the special style adopted in the treatment of the room, or whether it be a general sitting-room, a dining-room or bedroom.

The woodwork is carried out in the same way as ordinary panelling.

THE DINING-ROOM

The monumental sideboards of our forefathers, regrettable fact though it may be to many, are passing out of fashion, as may be found by anyone having such to dispose of by sale. In their place the adaptation of the American buffet or fixed sideboard as part of the permanent features of the dining-room is becoming a growing practice ; and there can be no doubt that this, when combined with a serving hatch giving communication from the pass pantry already described in detail, is a preferable accommodation, resulting in considerable saving of work.

A typical American buffet or sideboard is often built into a convenient recess, and consists of three separate parts, the outer two being of two parts, upper and lower. These outer portions in their pedestal or lower portions have shelves fitted with a pair of doors hung folding, either solid or glazed.

A pair of drawers are also fitted under the pedestal top. Over this the upper portion has two arched recesses for silver, or other articles, giving uninterrupted space from front to back, and above these are additional shelves usually enclosed with glazed folding doors hung folding.

The central portion is that which is combined with the sliding hatch to the pantry, and having a pair of folding doors panelled in wood, gives additional privacy to the occupants of the dining-room when the hatch is in use. Being fitted with shelves as well as a wide table top, the latter being at the same height as the pedestal tops and extending within the pantry, a sufficient width is thus obtained for the resting of the tray, the doors on the dining-room side remaining closed meanwhile, and the shelves affording accommodation for the smaller articles not accommodated by the tray. The saving in unnecessary walking in laying the dining-room table will be appreciated. As the cloths, and possibly the silver, are kept in the drawers of the sideboard, one or more of the drawers being lined with baize glued to the inner face of the drawer for that purpose, the glass and crockery which was removed to the pantry to be washed after the last meal and required for the forthcoming one, is stacked upon the shelves of the hatch. Everything having been prepared in this manner from the pantry side firstly, it then only remains to walk once from the pantry to the dining-room to receive them from that side instead of the customary repeated journeyings having to be made from pantry to dining-room.

The doors communicating to the hatch are then closed when the table is laid, and the courses of the meal passed and used dishes passed through the hatch as required. And at the end of the meal the table-cloths and unused articles are returned to the portions of the sideboard reserved for their accommodation.

SERVING HATCHES.—These in their simplest form consist of openings in the wall between the dining-room and kitchen, the opening being framed and lined, and fitted with an architrave as the door openings with a door hung folding therein.

But the door is sometimes found inconvenient when projecting outwards into either room, and consequently lift-up sashes are provided, running on pulleys attached to weights as for boxed-frame windows, the lower portion only being hung to open. A preferable form is that in which the whole door either slides upwards or sideways. This may be carried on runners run along the face of the wall, preferably that in the kitchen, or, where frame partitions divide the rooms, the door can be made to slide in a pocket formed in the interior of the partition. For the first a strip rebated to the requisite depth to take the door is nailed to grounds or fixing blocks, or wedges in the wall at top and bottom. The rebated runner should also be continued along the third or upright side, to serve as a stop for the sliding door.

Lifting sash to hatches may similarly be fixed with boxed frames in solid walls or pockets in frame partitions, but without considerable cutting; the two-piece door will be cheaper in solid brickwork, whilst the single door to slide up within a framed partition will provide greater convenience in the larger opening afforded.

However, direct openings from kitchen to dining-room, whilst indeed being great savers of walking, have nothing to commend them so far as privacy is concerned. The shelf space is also limited in depth, unless an additional table top is supplied. This, to be of a convenient form, should be of the lift-up pattern, so that it may be folded down against the wall when not in use. The supports should be hinged after the manner of the supports under folding tables. They may be either of the hinged bracket type, or longer supports hinged in a similar manner, and folding back one over the other when not in use, as in fly-rails under folding tables.

HATCHES AND LIFTS COMBINED.—When a cellar is provided for coals, a hatch in the kitchen is a great convenience when combined with a hand lift for the coals. This lift, necessitating some form of framing for its accommodation, affords facilities for its upper portion being used as a hatch without additional framing, being constructed in the following way. The lift works in a framing of 2″ by 2″ studs coming up in a convenient corner or other position in the kitchen. This is continued to the ceiling, and provided with doors at or near the floor level, and also at the level of the hatch sill. The lift itself is constructed of two portions, the lower being for the accommodation of the coal bucket and the upper containing shelves for use as previously described for a serving hatch. When in this position it is held in place by a catch from which it can again be released when required for use as a lift. The upper portion of the framing is panelled or sheated with matched lining in both rooms, and is fitted at its sill level with lift-up flaps, as already described.

DINING-ROOM FIREPLACES AND OVERMANTELS.—The essential feature of the dining-room fireplace, as distinguished from that in other rooms, will be that it should be wherever possible recessed, and where this is not possible it should be at least flush with the wall, on account of the space required for service between the walls and the backs of persons seated at table. The design will necessarily require to be adapted to such a position. Also a more severe character in the design will be in keeping in the dining-room than for that in the drawing-room, the surroundings of which may reasonably be expected to be of a more decorative order.

In the Georgian and Jacobean periods more attention was given to the overmantel than to the fireplace, with the result that their beauty exceeded their practical value. Some of the finest of the later Georgian were covered with fine carving by Grinling Gibbons, whose work is famous. His fireplace was usually found in conjunction with panelled rooms, of which they formed the crowning feature; and the carving included deeply-cut festoons of flowers, fruit and foliage. The cornice was of deep projection, and kept the same character as that of the panelling of the room; often having richly carved brackets supporting the cornice. On the pilasters and over the central panel occurred the chief carving, also the columns at the sides of the chimney breast were shaped into carved consoles.

Into the Jacobean even more intricate detail entered, there being much strap-work carving on the panels and mitreing of panel mouldings. In some cases the panel mouldings were worked upon the solid instead of being rebated into the framing.

However, except where it is particularly desired to copy any particular style, the tendency of modern work is to save dust-collecting surfaces by omitting detail, and to rely upon the natural beauty of the wood and proportion of the parts to give a restful, and at the same time a healthful, result. The main feature worthy of noting is that the fireplace should always be specially designed for the room by the designer of the building, and not purchased ready-made to fit it, and this will depend to a great extent upon the type of fireplace that is decided upon.

The plainest, and at the same time amongst the most serviceable, type of fireplace, for it should be borne in mind that a fireplace has other and more important duties even than looking architecturally beautiful, will be some form of the well type, in which the fire is built upon a grating covering a hollow in the hearth, and has no basket of grating in the ordinary old-fashioned sense. The breast and surround of such a fireplace, which is in elevation nothing more than an opening, which may have a flat or semicircular arch, is often faced with brick-work or tiles. This being of a very simple and plain nature would be out of keeping with anything of a very elaborate nature in the form of the overmantel.

In its very simplest form the overmantel may consist of merely a shelf about 10″ deep by ½″ to ¾″ thick, supported on plain square corbels or brackets cut to shape.

And where something a little more elaborate yet plain is desired above such a shelf, a flat panelling may be erected, terminating at the height of the picture rail, and having the picture rail carried over it as a cornice. The stiles and rails are cut out of 4″ by 1⅛″ stuff and the panels ½″ let into the rails as described under " Panelling."

As an alternative and a shade more decorative finish to the panels, an arched head may be added, either cut in the top rail or in a piece let in under the top rail, the thickness of the depth of the panel sinking.

Where a more ornate design, yet having the same " dust-proof " surfaces, is desired, ornamentation may very satisfactorily be introduced by inlay executed in woods of different colours from the ground work. Very fine examples of inlay work are to be seen in the Jacobean style. In executing inlay the pieces to be inlaid should be first cut out to the pattern desired and have the edges slightly bevelled and the under surface should be pierced with a bradawl to give a key for the glue. The pattern should then be laid on the surface into which it is to be inlaid and carefully marked round. The portions within the markings are then cut away with the chisel, great care being necessary not to cut away the edges beyond the marking, and to finish the bottom surface of the portion true and level.

It may be of interest here to note that *inlay* work is distinct from *marquetry*, as being cut out of solid wood and let into other solid wood as just described whilst marquetry is a process of veneering with marked pieces cut out, shaded and laid on.

The latter process consists of glueing a tracing of the design on to the sheet of veneer which is to form the ground, and other veneers to form the design are glued on the back with paper between them. They are then cut out with sloping edges to ensure a good fit on a marquetry cutter " Donkey." When the cutting is done, the design is laid on a board and the pieces shaded by dipping the veneer into hot sand. When this is completed, the design is glued down on to paper and laid by the cabinet maker.

PARQUETRY consists of geometric veneered work composed of diapers of the same wood.

For DINING-ROOM fireplaces some shelving and small cupboards are often desired, to serve as receptacles for smoking requisites. This

Fig. 182.

Fig. 181.

INTERIOR FITTINGS—CONCEALED DOOR IN PANELLING AND BRICK FIREPLACE WITH PANELLING.

INGLE-NOOKS

If recessed fireplaces in ingle-nooks are ever desirable in modern work, they will be more suitable in the dining-room than the drawing-room. But it may be doubted if it is ever very satisfactory, in rooms which depend upon an open fire for their heating, to recess that fire and shut

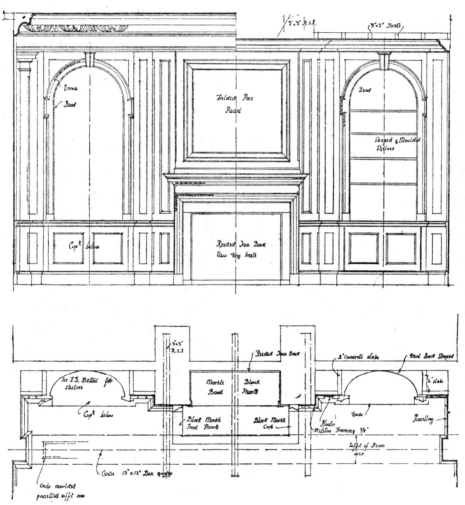

FIG. 187.—ARCHED RECESSES AT SIDE OF FIREPLACE.
Walter Cave, F.R.I.B.A., F.S.I., Architect.

it off in part from the room. In conjunction with some form of central heating, when the open fire becomes ornamental rather than practical, the recessed fire is a valuable adjunct and lends considerable attraction to a room ; but the logical reasons for the practice might be thought to have passed since the introduction of glass and the improvement in the draught-excluding properties of doors and windows. In old days when rooms were draughty at the best of times, some shelter in the form of screened seats must have been much appreciated, and at no point in the room could this more comfortably be obtained than round the fireplace. And as chimneys in those days were very large internally, and the fireplace openings high and wide, the result was that considerable volumes of smoke found their way into the room, and the hearth itself,

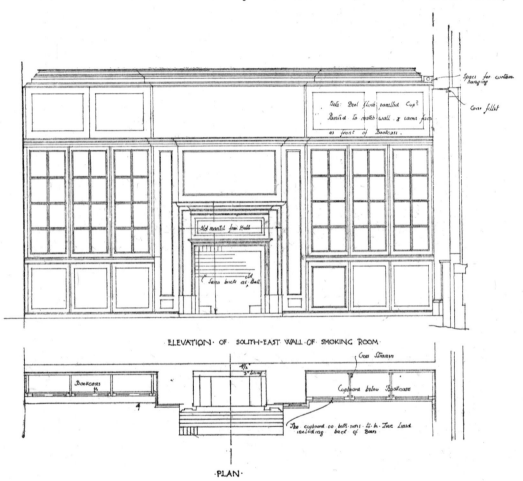

ELEVATION · OF · SOUTH-EAST · WALL · OF · SMOKING · ROOM ·

· PLAN ·

FIG. 188.—SMOKING-ROOM FITTINGS, by Walter Cave, F.R.I.B.A., Architect.

owing to the upward draught in the chimney, was often the portion of the room most free from smoke. Consequently the most coveted seat was that placed actually upon the hearth, and others were provided by means of settles with high backs and screened ends at right angles to the fireplace.

Such was the origin of the ingle-nook, and whether the feature is logically applicable to-day may be a matter of opinion. Nevertheless, artistic features seen perhaps in some old bar parlours delight us, and the

FIG. 183.—RECESSED DRAWING-ROOM FIREPLACE.

FIG. 184.—DINING-ROOM FIREPLACE.

desire to introduce something of the same nature into our homes is very natural ; and in the dining-room where it will serve as a cosy place to which to withdraw after the meal is finished, the ingle-nook has still a reason for a continued existence.

Also for constructional reasons, the fireplace being recessed to give width of floor space, the chimney stack is often projected beyond the main wall of the building. This has the result of necessitating some form of arch over the fireplace internally, and the basis of the ingle-nook is thereby supplied. And if the recess for the chimney breast be enlarged on both sides, and at the same time a little more depth added, space will thus be provided for two settees to be formed in the recess on either side of the fireplace. These may be formed of a front and back rail out of 5″ by 1″ stuff, resting on 2″ square bearers nailed to the walls at either end, where the recess provides walls at both ends. The seat and back are constructed of 1″ single boards or 1″ boards jointed together 1′ 6″ wide, the back being sloped. The arm rests shown, where walls occur, rest on bearers plugged to the walls.

The back may be either plain or panelled, flush beaded panels being the most comfortable. And in either case a moulded or chamfered capping should be housed over the top of the back. It is important to notice that the back should not be of a less height, measured from the seat, than 3′ 6″, in order to prevent the capping from coming into contact with the head of a person using the seat.

A simple design may depend almost entirely upon its proportions for a dining-room fireplace and ingle-nook. In this the seats are formed in the manner last described, but the ends are carried by an upright beam supporting the beam over the ingle-nook. Above the back of the seat, which consists of a 5″ rail surmounted by a 1″ rounded cap to match the shelf over the fireplace, plain, square-edged panelling is run round and over the fireplace having 4″ stiles and rails, the two panels over the fireplace on either side of the central panel having the top rails arched as shown. A feature of this design, giving additional usefulness, is that owing to the breaking back of the brickwork to form the flue, a space is provided behind the back of the panels on either hand of the central one. These, having the panels run in grooves, form cupboards. The cupboard backs and sides are formed of matched lining, and have shelves on bearers fixed within. The seat end is also formed of a square panel framed in between a top and bottom rail, which are run from and mortised into the post supporting the main beam and a 4″ square post at the outer edge of the seat. The ceiling of the ingle is panelled to match the panelling over the mantelshelf with the exception that the rails are bolection mould in place of square. For light a window is pierced in the wall, over the left-hand seat, the panels at the sides of the window being spaced to match those at the opposite side.

In another design for an ingle the chimney breast is entirely of brickwork, having a shelf run along at a height of 4′ 6″ from the hearth, and above this the flue is panelled with three square panels bounded by 4″ posts at each end. On either hand of these posts there is a recess panelled at the sides and back. In this design the seat consists of a log box, having a hinged lid in the top, plain dovetailed sides and a chamfered skirting run round the bottom. The back is of 3″ matched and V-jointed boarding, capped by a plain rounded edge board, which is also the window board of the window cut in above the seat back.

FIREPLACES IN PANELLING.—Overmantels in panelling often become little more than an adaptation of the panelling to form a more pronounced surround to the tile, brick or marble surround of the fireplace interior, the design of the panelling being as little interfered with as may be. Fig. 189 shows such a fireplace treatment, in which the surround adjoining the marble is formed of a plain fascia, having its joint with the marble surround concealed by a cover mould as shown in the details. The outer and upper edge of this fascia is rebated under an edging moulded to the same detail as the panelling and mitred and tongued at the corners, and ending at the base upon a chamfered plinth. Above this edging mould a wide rail carries the narrow shelf composed of a $1\frac{1}{2}$″ board with a moulding planted on the outer edge. This rail also becomes the bottom rail of the panelling above, the middle rail of the panelling to the room being fixed at a lower level ; but the rails of both wall and fireplace and the surface of the wall panelling and the fireplace fascia and surround are all worked to the same line. The shelf is rebated on its top edge to receive the rail above it, mortised to fit ; and on its under face a chase mortise receives the lower rail. The angles are mitred and feathered. Single-width boards should be used for the fascia, which is square rebated, the horizontal board being run across the vertical ones.

CARVED MANTELPIECES having a rich effect, but similarly treated in that they have no actual projection as a chimney breast, are sometimes formed as part of a feature composing the whole end or side of a room. The room is panelled in white, having long panels in its upper portion capped by a carved frieze and moulded cornice. The middle rail is widened out and carries a dado rail moulding, and a short panel comes below, and is terminated by a bottom rail and skirting. Between the panels is a boxed pilaster of shallow projection bolection moulded. The fireplace fitment carrying out the same scheme consists of a cover mould at the top of the marble interior, above which is a framed horizontal panel with carved moulding, and above this a shelf of 6″ projection by 4″ deep, having a moulded edge. Above this is a rectangular moulded and carved panel, having in its centre a circular convex mirror.

At the sides of the fireplace similar pilaster treatment to that obtaining in the room is carried out, and between these and the pilasters in the angle of the room, in place of the upper panels already mentioned, are recesses fitted with shelves and hung with glazed doors having diagonal panes carried with splay-jointed bars. The lower panels at the sides

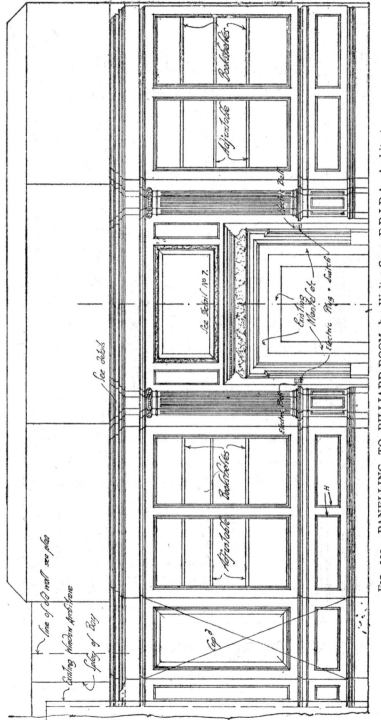

FIG. 190.—PANELLING TO BILLIARD-ROOM, by Walter Cave, F.R.I.B.A., Architect.

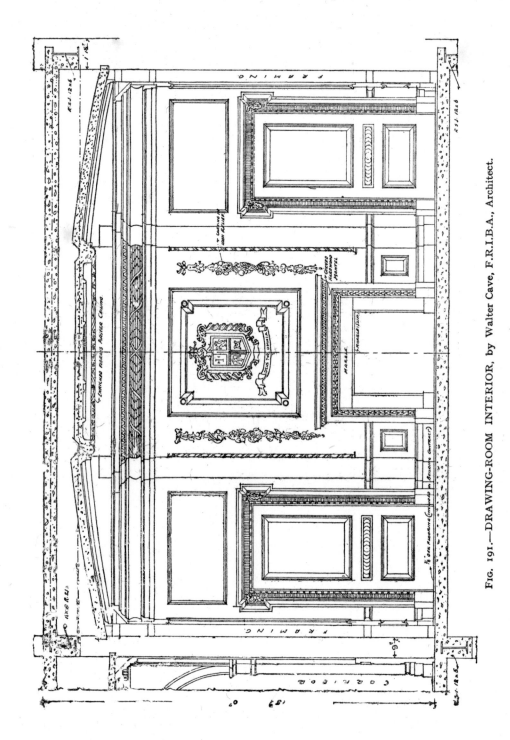

FIG. 191.—DRAWING-ROOM INTERIOR, by Walter Cave, F.R.I.B.A., Architect.

FIG. 189.—PANELLED CHIMNEY BREAST.

of the fireplace are also hung with doors, but panelled in wood to form closed cupboards. The upper cupboards serve as either book-shelves of china cabinets.

THE HALL

The hall may be said to offer more opportunities for architectural furnishings than any other part of a house. In fact, a properly treated hall will leave little to be desired in the way of movable furniture.

Much may be made of the staircase if it be of an open type, and especially if planned in conjunction with a fireplace in such a manner that the strings and panelling under will form a convenient back to a seat either at the side or facing the fire. Here again constructive necessities may be made to form an ingle-nook which may be described as justifiable. For example, if a staircase be run across a fireplace, either on the slope in the flight or as a landing, a recess is formed in a natural manner out of the constructive necessities of the staircase. An ingle would be appropriate where the stairs starting at the right-hand side reach a landing at a height of 6' 6", which is continued across the length of one side of the hall. Under this gallery could be placed the hall fireplace, and above a handrail filled in below with half-timbering uprights and braces having plaster worked in flush between them. To the right of the fire a seat is then fixed which is continued at right angles to finish at the end of a cabinet framed against the side of the stairs. The newels of the stairs could be carried up as square posts and terminate against beams carrying the ceiling.

Another form of combined ingle and staircase is one in which the gallery becomes an organ loft. In this case the stairs start in a direction at right angles to the wall on which the fireplace is situated, taking a right-angle turn on a quarter-space landing and then continuing upwards in a direction parallel to the chimney breast. Under the quarter-space landing a cupboard is built in, and under the flight, parallel to the chimney breast, seats are fitted on either hand to form the ingle-nook. All the newels are run up to the ceiling as square posts, and the gallery which forms the organ loft runs along the whole length of one side of the hall, being supported on brackets and open beams and joists. By this planning a very deep ingle is provided, and an architectural effect of exceptional character. Above the seat on one side of the ingle the wall is pierced for a three-light window, so that the ingle is well lit.

A more simple design for the hall of a small country house is so arranged that the fireplace is placed across the outer angle of the hall, and the stairs run at right angles to the outside wall. The front door giving entrance to the hall is situated on the wall which runs parallel to the stairs, and the fireplace crosses the angle made by this wall and the outer wall. The bottom newels of the staircase are 6" square solid posts, carried up to a beam running parallel to the outer wall. And against the stairs is placed a seat having a sloped back which is capped by a chamfered rail forming the outer string of the stairs. In this chamfered rail the balusters are also terminated, giving the lower steps of the stairs interiorly an unusual form of string. The seat is $1\frac{1}{2}''$ thick, having a lift-up lid hinged in its centre, and is terminated in a shaped pew end, through which it is mortised and pinned with wedges.

The pew end is housed into the newel post ; and the beam above gives definition to the space, which may be described as an ingle-nook. The fireplace consists of a brick breast arched with a semicircular arch, having above it a plain shelf carried on $4''$ square brackets with a square panelled overmantel, terminating in a cornice, consisting of the plain chamfered member of the top of the door architrave carried round as a picture rail. The front of the seat is plain boarded fixed to a batten nailed to the floor, and terminated on the one hand at the cut pew end and on the other against the outer wall, which has a batten for nailing to. The back of the seat is supported by a rail run from the pew end and fixed to the framing under the outer string of the stairs. The back of the seat is formed of match and V-jointed boarding, sloped and nailed at the bottom to a bevelled batten on the seat top. The lift-up flap in the seat top being provided with a sunk ring serves as a log or rug box. Into the newel post and beam over are tenoned cut brackets, the wall on which the other end of the beam rests having a half post, and a similar bracket let into it and the beam over in the same way.

DRAWING-ROOM

MANTELPIECE.—A more decorative fireplace and overmantel will be in keeping in the drawing-room, or even if not more decorated, at least one in which the detail is not of so bold a nature as is suitable for the dining-room. And as it is likely that there will be more ornaments in the form of china, photographs and vases, the design should include a certain amount of shelving. Also there is a feeling for mirrors, whether for the reflection of the ornaments or of person, consequently a certain proportion of the overmantel surface should be of mirror, in either one large sheet or in several small pieces. The mirror when in a large sheet should be placed centrally in the overmantel, being backed with match boarding and let into stiles and rails, and have a mitred moulding sprigged on to keep it in position. The same treatment on a smaller scale will also apply to smaller mirrors, which may be inserted in alcoves or arched recesses, having the arch supported by small turned columns or balusters resting upon bracketed shelves for the ornaments to be stood upon. The arch is cut out of $\frac{1}{2}''$ stuff, having a moulded cup housed down over the top or rebated to receive the top and tenoned into the cap of the column at its lower edge. Under the shelf cut and moulded brackets should support the shelf, being tenoned into it and the overmantel face.

A carved mantel having a rich effect yet of simple detail is shown in Fig. 189. This is built up of a moulded top imposed on a curved architrave cut in the solid over a fascia framed into its underside and having a cavetto mould and fillet to cover the joint. The breasts are framed up of square-faced pilasters on square-edged bases, and have carved and moulded brackets and pilasters superimposed. The architrave shaped out of the solid is constructed as shown in Fig. 192.

The underside of the top is grooved to take the rebate cut on the

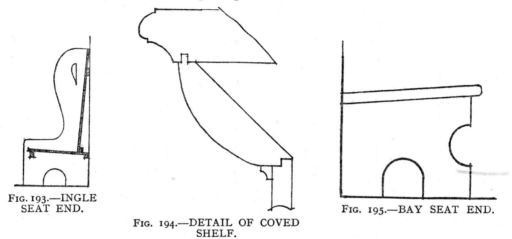

FIG. 193.—INGLE SEAT END.

FIG. 194.—DETAIL OF COVED SHELF.

FIG. 195.—BAY SEAT END.

top edge of the curved portion, and its bottom edge likewise being grooved to take the rebate cut on the fascia.

The woods suitable for mantelpieces are, for very cheap work, deal, American pine, and where panels occur, sycamore also, mahogany, oak, Cannelle noir and New South Wales Brigalow.

WINDOW SEATS.—In the drawing-room it is often desired to use the

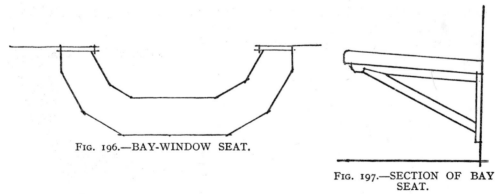

FIG. 196.—BAY-WINDOW SEAT.

FIG. 197.—SECTION OF BAY SEAT.

window for additional sitting accommodation; especially is this the case when the window is a bay.

The simplest form of window seat where the sills of the windows are at the customary height consists of a seat top formed of two or more boards butt-jointed or rebated together, framed and screwed to battens and supported on gallows brackets screwed to the underside of the cross battens and the walls. Horizontal bearers also support the ends plugged to wall where the window is placed in a recessed opening. Though a point worthy of note is that the seat will be found more comfortable to sit on if the outer edge be kept 1″ higher from the floor than the edge against the wall, as shown in Fig. 197.

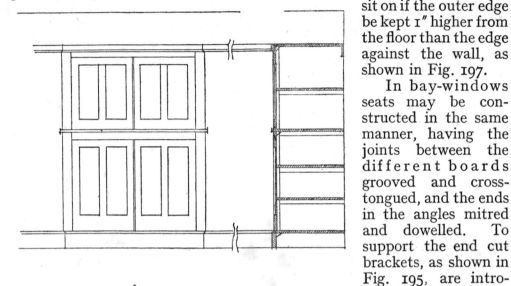

FIG. 198.—CORNER CUPBOARD.

In bay-windows seats may be constructed in the same manner, having the joints between the different boards grooved and cross-tongued, and the ends in the angles mitred and dowelled. To support the end cut brackets, as shown in Fig. 195, are introduced, being grooved and rebated into the underside of the seat top or, where a more elaborate finish is desired, the end may be carried up as a pew end, being grooved to receive the tenon cut on the end of the seat.

CORNER CUPBOARDS, resembling cabinets but of fixed type, are often desired in drawing-rooms. These in their cheapest form may consist only of top and front, having the angle formed by the two walls for the back. A framing of a $\frac{3}{4}$″ top and $\frac{1}{2}$″ stiles and 1″ base is first fixed to the walls across the angle, the outer edges of the stiles being splayed to fit against the wall and being nailed to angle blocks fixed to wall plugs. From the top of these along the walls are run bearers fixed to the walls, on to which the top is nailed. Doors, either plain, panelled or glazed, are hung in the stiles with rebated meeting rails. Shelves may be fitted in as desired on proper chamfered bearers.

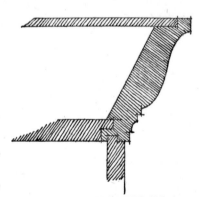

FIG. 199.—CORNICE TO CUPBOARD.

BOOK-CASES.—Whilst the living-room—or, where there is one, the library—is the more customary place for the accommodation of books,

FIG. 192.—DRAWING-ROOM FIREPLACE, SHOWING COVED MANTEL TOP.

[C.J.—III.

yet a certain number of *belles lettres* and special books will be in keeping
with the furnishing of a
drawing-room. And for
these, built-in book-cases
may well be provided. These
will consist of two part
upper and lower or shelves
and pedestal, and the shelves
may be open or, if preferred,
be enclosed with glazed
doors, hinged to open outwards.

Where convenient recesses
occur, as is frequently the case
at the side of chimney breasts,
very little more is necessary
than shelves open at the back
and resting on bearers or rebated into the standards at
the ends with divisions cut in
between the shelves. The
skirting may be continued
round the base, and the
bottom shelf fixed at a height
flush with the top of the
skirting. The top may consist of a single board similar
to the shelves but thicker,
grooved to take the divisions
and secret dovetailed to the
sides or standards. Or, if
desired, a cornice may be
fitted in between this top and
a false top, as shown in Fig.
199. The joint between the
top, the front and the
cornice should be concealed
by the rebate in the bottom
member of the cornice in
the manner shown. The
pedestal, which should project at least 6″ beyond the
upper portion, may be filled
with shelves, spaced farther
apart for larger books, or
have one row of drawers immediately under it and cupboard fronts below.

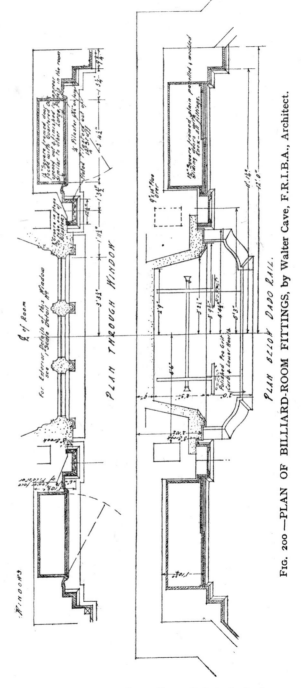

Fig. 200—PLAN OF BILLIARD-ROOM FITTINGS, by Walter Cave, F.R.I.B.A., Architect.

Where the fitting is placed on the face of a wall in such a manner that its ends are exposed, a back should be framed, and well fitted to act as a stiffener, and to prevent the case from rocking. This is made of framed panels, the stile and top and bottom rails being rebated into it and screwed from the back. If the case is over 4′ 0″ in width, the shelves should be divided by intermediate standards. The shelves, where loose, which is a preferable method, are rested on patent fittings, for which slots are cut in the standards. Finger pins are also used for this purpose, which are brass castings having a circular head with a short pin attached ;

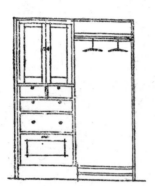

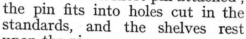

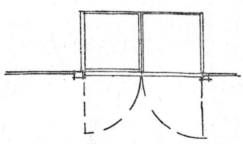

Fig. 201.—BUILT-IN WARDROBE.

the pin fits into holes cut in the standards, and the shelves rest upon the pin.

The standards are $1\frac{1}{4}$″, and the shelves $\frac{1}{2}$″ to $\frac{3}{4}$″ ; the top of the book-shelves and the pedestal top $1\frac{3}{4}$″. The bottom is rebated into the bottom rail of the back and into the skirting or base, and blocked underneath.

THE BEDROOM

FIXED WARDROBES.—The old-fashioned wardrobe, very often of beautiful construction in itself, is fast growing obsolete. With the exception of the piano and perhaps also the sideboard, it was generally the largest piece of furniture, and was particularly inconvenient, owing to the fact that it had to be carried up the stairs. To prevent this, and at the same time to avoid dust collection and removal, wardrobe fitments in modern work are frequently fixtures.

Where the rooms are divided by lath and plaster partitions, this matter is much simplified by building the partition double, and dividing the space enclosed equally by a cross partition and fitting a doorway in each on opposite sides. The doors are hung in the same manner as those to the rooms ; and the interior of the cupboard may be provided with a shelf or shelves on bearers, that at the back being a 6″ rail fitted with clothes hooks.

If more elaborate fittings are desired, these may consist of pedestals of drawers and hanging spaces, provided with hangers on rails with shelves over. A built-in wardrobe of this nature is shown in Fig. 136, where the left-hand portion consists of a pedestal with cupboards fitted with shelves above. The pedestal is framed up of $\frac{3}{4}''$ sides and top, having a base mitred around and rebated to receive the bottom. The sides are rebated to the top, and drawers are fitted in underneath, being divided by $\frac{1}{2}''$ rails and run on hardwood runners. Above the pedestal are hung two doors to open outwards, and around the whole, and tenoned into the underside of the cornice, is an architrave finishing down on to the base.

On the right-hand side one or two $\frac{1}{2}''$ shelves are fixed on bearers and having inverted hooks for clothes-hangers. On the floor beneath this are two rails fixed at $6''$ apart, one $4''$ higher than the other as a boot rack.

The whole is enclosed by a pair of doors of detail, and with architrave to match those to the room. Or, alternatively, the panels may be replaced by full-length mirrors.

MANTELPIECES TO BEDROOMS.—Wood overmantels to bedrooms require to be of very simple design, it being often a matter of opinion if anything more than a wooden shelf is required. Where this is so, and an overmantel is fitted, it may be made use of as a setting for a mirror. Mirrors, when fixed against walls, it should be noted, should be backed by waterproof building paper and matchboarding screwed to the frame, in this case the panel stiles.

'THE BEDROOM'

FIG. 202.—BUILT-IN FITMENTS.

DRESSING-CLOSETS.— Where the space is not sufficient to permit of a dressing-room, a closet for that purpose may often be provided between double partitions, or in a convenient corner. This should have a window in one wall, and where running water is possible, an angle basin should be included. Above this an angle cupboard for the shaving requisites, having the front panel formed of a convex mirror, with two side mirrors hinged to the sides of the cupboard as shown, in which position they may be adjusted at satisfactory angles. Above are shelves for glasses, shaving brushes, etc., and under the central mirror a shallow drawer with narrow divisions for ties.

On the opposite wall of this dressing-closet a fitment is fixed having either hanging cupboard space or drawers, and on the wall running between these a fixed chest of drawers is formed. The hanging cupboard consists of double doors hung folding in a rebated frame, the top rail of which carries a cornice, into the top of which is rebated the lining forming the top. A hanging rail and shelves are fitted on bearers at

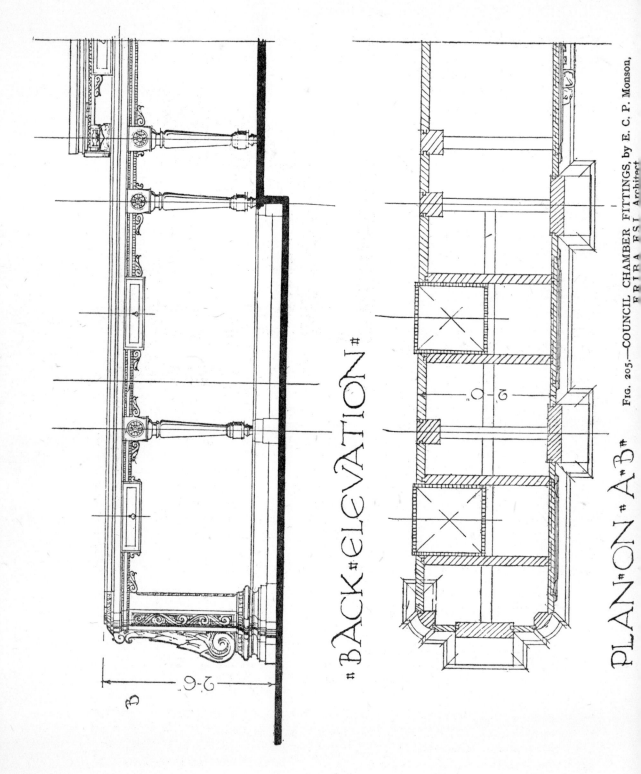

BACK#ELEVATION#

2'-6"

B

PLAN#ON#A#B#

G'-0"

FIG. 205.—COUNCIL CHAMBER FITTINGS, by E. C. P. Monson, F.R.I.B.A., F.S.I., Architect.

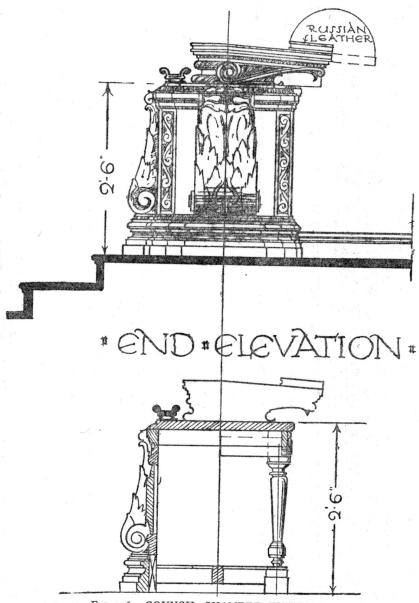

2'6"

RUSSIAN LEATHER

⁜ END ⁜ ELEVATION ⁜

2'6"

Fig. 206.—COUNCIL CHAMBER FITTINGS,
by E. C. P. Monson, F.R.I.B.A., F.S.I., Architect.

Joints Used in Fittings

Bevelled Jointing is used in forming angles, by cutting the pieces to be joined on the splay and glueing and clamping together with hand screws. It is used in all cases where either angles or rounded faces are desired to fitments, and wherever possible, to prevent opening of the joint, it should also be tongued.

Dowelled Joints are those having cylindrical pieces of wood from $1\frac{1}{2}''$ to $2\frac{1}{2}''$ long, generally of beech, inserted into holes bored in the edges to be jointed.

Dowelled Butt Jointing is used for lengthening timbers such as cornice mouldings, casings round girders, and pilasters in panelling.

Dowelled Clamping is used for jointing long grain to end grain, as in edgings to table tops.

Coopered Joints are those used in jointing curved pieces to form cylinders as in columns and curved panels in framing.

Matched Joints, in distinction from tongued joints, have a tongue worked on the solid, whereas the latter have a loose tongue inserted in a groove cut for its reception. They occur in panelling division rails.

Ploughed and Tongued Jointing is the method in which a cross tongue is used where a strong joint is desired, as in connection with the coopered joint. Feather tongues are not so strong as tongues cut across the grain, known as cross tongues. The joint gains additional strength by being glued. The tongues prevent the passage of air and light.

Secret Slot Joints are used for jointing shelves. The screw being sunk in a slot assists in enabling the jointed materials to be used at once after glueing, planing and fitting being rendered possible thereby. They are also used in fitting of brackets in fireplaces and panelling, and almost every kind of fitting in which strong and secret fixing is desired.

Rubbed Joints are butt-jointed square edges formed by trueing the edges to be jointed, painting with glue and rubbing together to get a close fit.

Varieties of Mortise and Tenon

A Double Mortise and Tenon consists of a stub mortise and tenon joint haunched out to form two tenons. They are used in fittings such as sideboards, the ends of which are mortised to form several tenons, as the method is found to be stronger than dowelling.

Barefaced Mortise and Tenon.—For jointing a rail which is thinner than the stile, when to shoulder both sides would cut away too much of the rail, only one side is cut, and the joint termed a barefaced mortise and tenon.

Foxtail Wedging is a dovetail tenon formed by inserting the ends of wedges into saw cuts in the tenon. When the tenon is knocked home, the wedges are driven in by the pressure against the bottom of the mortise.

The mortise is cut splayed out wider at the bottom than at the outer edge to take the new wedge shape of the tenon when expanded by the wedges.

HAUNCHED MORTISE AND TENON is a stub mortise and tenon given additional strength by means of a shoulder being cut in the tenon for which a stub mortise is cut. It is a joint used in panelling and fitment doors.

LONG AND SHORT SHOULDER MORTISE AND TENON is used in rebated framing, where the stile has a rebate, and the tenon has one shoulder cut back farther than the other to accommodate the rebate. It is mostly used in panellings and framing, having mouldings planted on over the rebate to hold the panel in place.

PINNING is a type of dovetailing and mortising combined, and is used where inner framing is covered with veneer. In formation it consists of a number of square tenons being cut to fit through mortises on the board with which it is desired to make a right-angle joint.

THROUGH MORTISE AND TENON is used in heavy framing and for upper and lower rails of panelling. The tenon projects right through the stile, and, the mortise being cut wider at the outside than the inside, the joint is wedged up.

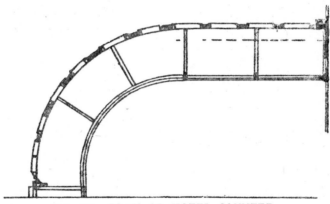

FIG. 208.—PLAN OF HOTEL COUNTER.
For elevation see Fig. 204.

TONGUED SHOULDER MORTISE AND TENON is used in lobby and vestibule doors, and is a mortise and tenon having in addition tongues cut in the shoulders which prevent the springing of the shoulder.

TWIN MORTISE AND TENONS have two tenons cut in thick stuff side by side, as used in door lock rails, the wide haunching between allowing room for the lock.

STUB MORTISE AND TENON, as used in doors the tenon is reduced in width, and coming at the end of a rail allows of a portion of the rail being left to resist lengthwise strain and keep the rail in place. Legs of furniture are also jointed in this manner to the under rail.

VARIETIES OF DOVETAIL JOINTS

COMMON DOVETAIL is used for jointing two pieces of wood at right angles where there is to be a downward strain, as in brackets. It consists

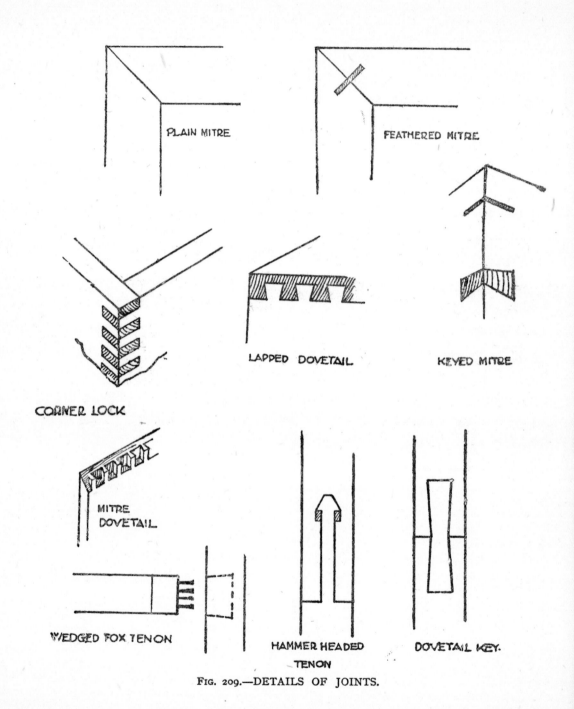

PLAIN MITRE

FEATHERED MITRE

CORNER LOCK

LAPPED DOVETAIL

KEYED MITRE

MITRE DOVETAIL

WEDGED FOX TENON

HAMMER HEADED TENON

DOVETAIL KEY.

FIG. 209.—DETAILS OF JOINTS.

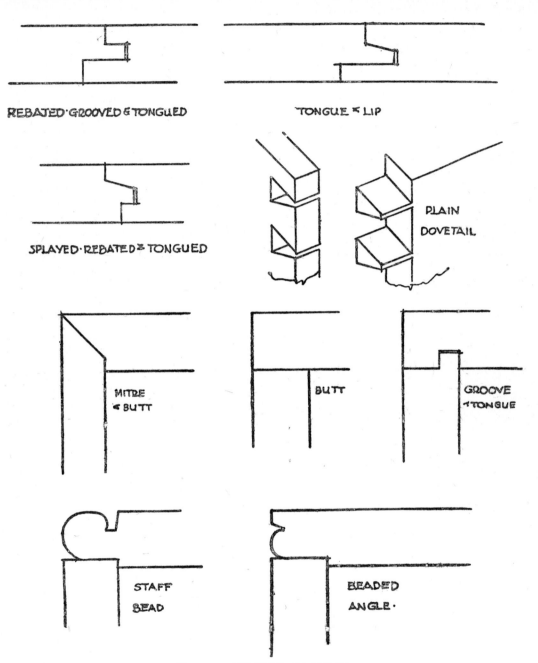

REBATED·GROOVED & TONGUED

TONGUE & LIP

SPLAYED·REBATED & TONGUED

PLAIN
DOVETAIL

MITRE
& BUTT

BUTT

GROOVE
& TONGUE

STAFF
BEAD

BEADED
ANGLE·

FIG. 210.—DETAILS OF JOINTS.

of a wedge-shaped tenon cut on the upper piece fitting into a corresponding cut on the end of the lower one, the joint showing on the face of both pieces.

COMMON HOUSED DOVETAILING is used in framing one board to the face of another at right angles, and consists of a wedge-shaped tenon cut along the length of the end of one board to fit by being slid into a wedge-shaped groove in the other. It is used for fixed shelving in fitments.

CHAPTER VI

VERANDAHS, BALCONIES AND GARDEN FURNITURE

Verandahs—Details of Construction—Proportion of Columns—Frieze and Cornice—Balusters and Handrail—Floors—Angle Brackets—Roofs—Balconies—Sleeping Porch—Glazed Screens—Trellis Work—Gates and Garden Furniture—Garden Wall Doors—Lych-gates and Wicket-gates.

A VERANDAH is defined as an open portico, and a portico as a piazza, gallery or covered walk. Therein may lie the reason for the confusion of the terms, for the names *verandah*, *porch* or *portico*, *piazza* and *balcony* are frequently used indiscriminately for the same feature. In England any adjunct to a building having one or more sides open to the weather is improperly described as a *verandah*, whilst in America the name of *porch* is similarly applied. Again, *piazza* and *loggia* are often used where verandah is meant.

In order to clear up this indefiniteness it may be well as a first step to enquire shortly into the origin of the terms and to distinguish between the separate purposes. And at the outset it may be laid down as a broad distinction between verandah and balcony, that the first is properly descriptive of a roofed open space on the ground floor of a building, whilst the second applies to an open portion of a building which may or may not be roofed, but which must be supported on columns or brackets.

The reason for this distinction is that, whilst the word *verandah* or *veranda* is comparatively modern in English, not being in general use before the early nineteeth century, it was known earlier in India, and in modern Hindustani appears as *verand*, and in Malayan as *baranda*. At the same time it is of European origin, being found as early as the fifteenth and sixteenth centuries in Spanish and Portuguese, and apparently is derived from the Latin *vara*, a forked pole or rod.

The point, however, for the present purpose is that, though it was taken by the early Portuguese navigators to the East, it was from the East that it was brought to England and used in description of portions of houses at a time when many persons, retiring from active life in India, desired to embody, in their homes in England, certain features to which they had become used in India. Among these was the verandah, and, as their houses in India had been of the bungalow type, which is one built on one floor only, the verandah must consequently have been built on the ground floor, so that its application to any part of a building in any other position must be inaccurate.

On the other hand, the term *balcony* clearly defines a platform projecting from a building supported by columns or brackets, being derived from the Italian *balcone*, from *balca*, a scaffold.

Whereas the word *portico*, being derived from the Latin *porticus*, properly describes a portion of a building giving entrance to that building and having a roof carried by columns. It may consist of a small space, or, as in the Greek and Roman temples, it may be the entire front of the building; but by origin it is properly used only in description of that part of a building used as an entrance, the term *porticus* being used to distinguish the entrance portion of a temple from that inner portion known as the *porticum*.

In America the term *piazza* is loosely applied also in place of the proper word *verandah*. This, however, is properly an open square or place in an Italian town, from the Latin *platea*, meaning a broad space. These squares were usually surrounded by a colonnade or arcade. So that, whilst it is loosely used in description of any covered arcade, it is correct as applied to modern building work perhaps in description only of spaces surrounded by columns or pergolas in garden architecture.

Therefore, as a general rule, whilst it seems more satisfactory to have a particular name for use in description of a particular portion of a building, and one name only wherever possible, in this matter we have derivation and origin to assist us.

THE VERANDAH

Consequently, verandah is defined as a portion of a building having a prepared floor covered by a roof which may be flat or pitched, and the roof supported by posts or columns in such a manner that one or more sides are open to the outside air. In some instances a verandah, where the main purpose is a sitting-out place as distinct from a covered entrance porch, may be roofed by means of the floor of the rooms above being projected over and supported by the verandah posts or columns. But here the distinction lies in the use to which the space is to be put.

WEST ELEVATION·
FIG. 211.

For example, it may be that a plan will lend itself to the extension of the slope of a main roof on one front down to the level of a line running round at the level of the heads of the ground-floor windows. By this expedient, in the first instance, additional floor space will be gained in the rooms on the first floor above, which will also be increased by the method of lighting which will become necessary, viz. by dormer windows. Also by continuing the roof line in one sweep a roofing to the verandah is provided at the same time as the artistic appearance of the building is enhanced.

Again, it may be found desirable to project a room or rooms on the

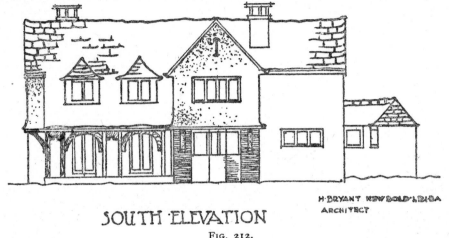

SOUTH ELEVATION
FIG. 212.

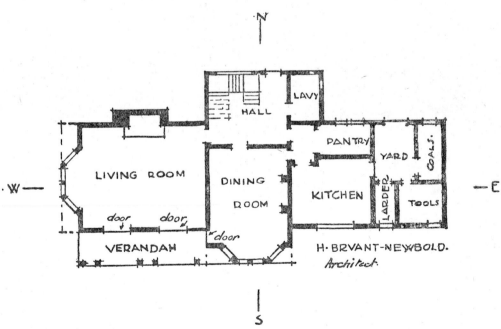

FIG. 213.—PLAN AND ELEVATION SHOWING VERANDAH ARISING OUT OF CONSTRUCTION.

first floor over bay-windows to the ground-floor rooms, and a small verandah space may be provided by this projection.

Such forms of verandah, being a natural outcome of the design and its constructive necessities, will always be more happy in appearance than anything in the nature of an after-thought and an extraneous application, which verandahs having a projection from the main building, and separately roofed, will always be. By this is meant verandahs so situated that both the building and the verandah would be entities without each other. A verandah with a sloping or flat roof applied outside and beyond the line of the main walls of a building will always have such an appearance, as may be seen from a glance at Fig. 214, where the verandah is necessary only as an outdoor sitting space and forms no essential part of the design of the main building. This could, except

FIG. 214.—AN APPLIED VERANDAH.

from the point of view of propinquity, have been built removed from the building, when it would have become a summer-house. In good design, verandahs should not be summer-houses stuck on to buildings like sealing-wax applied to the knots of postal packages; but, wherever possible, they should grow out of the constructive necessities of the design in the manner referred to briefly above.

The location of a verandah will always be dependent upon the plan of the building and the requirements of its occupants, and upon these requirements will also depend its aspect. For instance, it may be that it is required as an adjunct to a dining-room in summer, and the space used for taking meals upon, in which case it will be most conveniently placed so that access may be gained to it from the dining-room. On the other hand, it may be desired to use the verandah as a sitting-out place where the sunshine may be made the most of in the colder seasons and at the same time as a shaded place in summer-time, in which case it will be best situated adjacent to the living- or drawing-room.

It will be obvious that the most serviceable verandah will be one to which access may be gained from both dining- and living-rooms, and which will consequently lend itself to use for all of the purposes mentioned above—though, in these circumstances, the matter of aspect will provide additional difficulties to the problem.

A way in which access may be gained to the verandah from both sitting- and dining-room is shown in Fig. 213, where French windows are provided from both rooms opening on to the verandah; but, as in this instance the dining-room and longer wall of the sitting-room face due south, it will be readily seen that at the hottest part of any day, in any season of the year, the verandah would face directly towards the sun. The only point which can be made favourably in this matter is that the eaves over the verandah, being low, would cast a shadow over most of the verandah during the hottest season, when the sun would be higher at midday than it would during the cooler periods.

But if it is desired to use the verandah for breakfasting out of doors, as is a frequent practice in America, it will be necessary to place it on the eastern elevation of the building, so that the early sun may visit it ; and, so placed, the problem of shade at times later in the day will be solved by the position of the main walls of the building. Such a location will also secure a cool dining-place for evening use in summer.

However, should it be desired to use the verandah as a sitting-out place only, the problem of gaining sunshine in the cooler periods and shade in summer becomes more difficult of solution. Perhaps the most that can be done in this respect with a verandah which runs along one elevation only is to make it as deep as possible and so render serviceable the shade cast by the eaves as referred to above, and also to so place it that it obtains some shade during the latter part of the day from a wall or filled-in end at its western end ; for it is during the later hours of the day in summer that opportunities for sitting out may be indulged in by the majority, and it is then when the accumulated heat is generally most oppressive. It should be unnecessary to add, were it not so often seen, that there is one aspect in which a verandah is entirely out of place, and this is facing north.

DETAILS OF CONSTRUCTION

Where a verandah is at the ground-floor level and the ground floor is not more than 2′ 0″ above the level of the ground line there does not appear much reason in filling in the spaces between the supports with railings. A handrail in such a position is scarcely necessary as a protection against falling, though it may have its uses for leaning either the elbows or the feet upon. But in America, where the ground floor is generally raised several feet above the ground line, the need of a handrail is more obvious. In such circumstances, the floor of the verandah, being over a hollow space below, will be constructed of wood, and where a double floor is formed having a rough flooring underneath the upper floor boards should be run in a direction from the building outwards and should be jointed in red lead and preferably also painted with white lead paint on the surface. In both cases, solid and boarded, the surface of the verandah floor should be sloped to fall outwards away from the building. And where the floor is raised several feet above the ground line and boarded as described, whatever design may be decided upon for the string course or table mould which is run round at the level of the verandah floor, a gutter to catch the rain-water should be provided at the outer edge of the verandah. This may be a sinking in the outer edge of the floor, or it may be so worked in that it becomes a top member of the string course, as shown in Fig. 215.

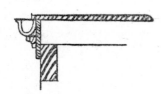

EXTERNAL·GUTTER
a

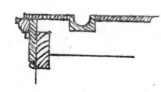

INTERNAL·GUTTER
b

FIG. 215.

SUPERSTRUCTURE.—The details of the construction of the superstructure will depend to a great extent upon the style chosen for the design of the rest of the building. Where this is classic, or of that style known as colonial in America, in which the verandah is seen at its best, circular columns will be indicated. These have turned posts, either springing from a base on the verandah floor, or they rest on a pedestal which forms a newel for the intermediate handrail. In either case the proportion of the columns will be a matter of great importance.

RULE FOR PROPORTION OF COLUMNS.—As a guide in designing classic columns in any of the four classic orders, Tuscan, Doric, Ionic or Corinthian, the following proportions of height to diameter will prove useful.

TABLE GIVING PROPORTIONS OF CLASSIC COLUMNS IN DIAMETERS AT THE BOTTOM END OF SHAFT

Order.	Base.	Shaft.	Capital.	Whole Column.	Architrave.	Frieze.	Cornice.
Tuscan	$\frac{1}{2}$	6	$\frac{1}{2}$	7	$\frac{1}{2}$	$\frac{7}{12}$	$\frac{2}{3}$
Doric	$\frac{1}{2}$	7	$\frac{1}{2}$	8	$\frac{1}{2}$	$\frac{3}{4}$	$\frac{3}{4}$
Ionic	$\frac{1}{2}$	$8\frac{1}{2}$	$1\frac{1}{6}$	9	$\frac{3}{4}$	$\frac{3}{4}$	$\frac{7}{8}$
Corinthian	$\frac{1}{2}$	$8\frac{1}{3}$	$1\frac{1}{6}$	10	$\frac{3}{4}$	$\frac{3}{4}$	1

The above table gives the height of the main divisions of each order in terms of the diameter measured at the bottom of the shaft; and, as will be seen, these main divisions in each order consist of a column which is composed of a shaft with base and capital or cap. Over this is an entablature which is made up of architrave, frieze and cornice. Roughly the entablature is generally about one-fourth the height of the column and the pedestal one-third.

Should there be a flat roof having a balustrading over the verandah to form a balcony to the upper rooms the proportion of this will to some extent be settled by the rules applying to handrail heights; but the foreshortening effect due to height should be borne in mind, and greater height and substantiality given than would be the case if constructed on the eye line or at the usual height of a handrail, which is below the eye line.

CONSTRUCTION OF COLUMNS.—Where circular columns form part of the verandah they may be turned out of the solid, but the practice is wasteful of timber, and the wood is almost certain to split down the grain; consequently the method is not recommended. A preferable method is that known as *cooper jointing*, in which the column is made up of strips having their outer surfaces consisting of arcs of the circle and jointed together with radiating joints. Each strip should be as narrow as may be, as the smaller they are the more likely to be better seasoned throughout. The

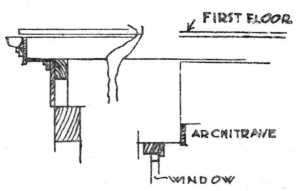

FIG. 216.—VERANDAH ROOF CONSTRUCTION.

strips are jointed together in their lengths either by being tongued and grooved, rebated or having a feather let into a groove. The whole is blocked and bracketed together, a half column prepared at a time and then jointed together.

The caps and bases are turned out of the solid with the grain horizontal. And where solid posts are used for columns they should be of redwood or cypress, as these stand best without cracking. As an additional preventive they should also be bored longitudinally through the centre.

THE CONSTRUCTION OF FRIEZE AND CORNICE.—The simplest form of roofing over a verandah is a flat roof consisting of short lengths of rafter run from the main wall to rest upon a plate carried over the heads of the posts or columns. The flat should have a pitch downwards of $\frac{3}{8}''$ to a foot away from the well to carry the rain-water to the gutter formed in the cornice. But where a more elaborate cornice and frieze is desired the plate carrying the ends of the rafters will be supported by upright studding framed up from a second plate carried on the heads of the columns. The columns, when built up in the manner described and carrying a balcony over, should be cored with studs, or, when even greater strength is required, with a steel joist or c.i. column. Within one of these hollow columns the rain-water down spout may be run from the gutter to the gulley.

The cornice and frieze is built up in sections, having the sections tongued and grooved where necessary.

BALUSTERS AND HANDRAIL.—Where a handrail is desired it should be framed in between the columns, or to finish against a base or pedestal where one is provided for the column to rest upon. In this case the handrail will generally be ramped up and the moulding continued round the pedestal at a higher level. The face of the pedestal may be panelled and provided with a base, or skirting.

The handrail and balusters are similar to those used internally, but the top of the handrail should be bevelled to slope outwards in order to throw off the rain-water in that direction. All joints should either be painted before being put together or jointed in red lead. A similar bevel should appear on the top of the lower rail, corresponding with the capping to the outer string in a staircase, and, instead of the balusters being housed into this rail or capping, as in a staircase, they should be scribed down on to the moulded or bevelled capping. The usual height for the handrail is 2' 6" from the floor, and the lower rail should be kept 2" above the floor, blocks being inserted under the rail at distances of from 4' 0" to 5' 0" to act as stiffeners. A balustrading may consist of a solid rail and under-rail having square balusters which are housed or mortised into the underside of the rail and butted or scribed down on to the lower rail and side-nailed. Rails should be of sizes suited to the design, those less than 4" by 4" being cut out of the solid. Balusters may be from $\frac{7}{8}$" by $\frac{1}{4}$" to $1\frac{1}{4}$" square and set from $1\frac{1}{4}$" apart. Turned balusters are cut out of stuff from 4" upwards.

OPEN FLOORING.—In situations where much snow or rain is to be expected verandah floors, where double, should have the upper flooring open jointed, the boards having square edges and being set about $\frac{3}{16}$" apart, the nails being driven in from the top. When the joints are matched they should be painted with thick white lead and oil just before the floor is laid.

When the sides of the verandah are enclosed in solid walls a narrow strip should be run round the outside edge of the floor having a groove worked in it to form a gutter. This gutter should be sloped and have holes for the discharge of the water.

STEPS TO VERANDAH.—When steps in wood are required to give access from the ground level to that of the verandah they should be supported on cut strings at 15" to 20" apart and resting at their lower end on a stone or concrete foundation wall. The treads may be either solid, when they are formed of $1\frac{1}{4}$" boards with rounded nosings and having the ends finished with a nosing planted on and mitred at the angle as in the case of a cut string to an indoor staircase; a scotia or cavetto mould is usually introduced under the nosing: the ends of the steps may be finished with a triangular panel, which is formed of a moulding planted on, or the panel may be formed of lattice work for ventilation. Or they may be formed of open-work slats 2″ wide by $\frac{7}{8}$″ thick nailed to three cut carriages.

UPRIGHT FRONTS AND SIDES OF RAISED VERANDAHS.—Where the verandah is raised above the ground level a solid pier is built under the columns or posts, and the intervening spaces are filled in with casings having lattice-work panels for ventilation. The lattice consists either of strips $\frac{1}{4}$″ by $1\frac{1}{4}$″ nailed over each other at right angles, the upright strip being the outer. The openings should be of the same width as the strips, and square, and the strips should be nailed at their points of crossing. Alternatively strips $\frac{3}{4}$″ thick by $2\frac{1}{2}$″ wide may be halved together, forming a more substantial lattice, but at the same time a more costly one. In cheaper work the lattice is first fixed in position and the casing nailed on afterwards to hide the ends of the lattice; but a better method of construction is to nail the lattice to the casing or frame, afterwards fixing the whole to grounds within the opening.

MOVABLE FLOORS.—Balcony floors having a lead or zinc covering should be provided with movable flooring consisting of duckboards formed of battens and cleats. The slabs should be 4″ square, laid $\frac{1}{4}$″ apart and nailed to $1\frac{3}{8}$″ cleats, which should be blocked up from the roof covering and laid loose and left in sections of a convenient size for moving.

SQUARE POSTS.—In certain designs circular columns would be out of place, and square posts will be found preferable. These, when over 4″ square, should be framed together to prevent cracks. When weights are to be supported they may be cored with steel joists or c.i. columns. Square-built joints at the angles will be the cheapest, but are likely to gape under the influence of the weather. To prevent this they may be plain mitred, though this will only effect an improvement in so far as the gape will appear on the angle rather than on the square face. The most secure form of joint for the boxed post will be that known as the *Feathered Mitre*, the joint being splayed and having its faces cut with a groove down which a hardwood strip, or feather, is run. The joint will be glued and kept in a clamp till set.

Alternately, the angles may be jointed with the *rebate and bead* joint or *rebated and staff bead*. These joints have an advantage in positions where it is impossible to clamp the work before being placed in position, but where it is necessary to fix it on the job. The effect of the bead is to cast a shadow over the joint and to conceal the gaping to some extent.

When panelled posts are desired a moulding may be sprigged on to the surface of the boards.

Solid or made-up square posts should never be let into the floor of the verandah, as the sinking will provide a hollow for the collection of rain-water, which will soon rot the foot of the post. They should be either rested flush on the floor, having the foot,

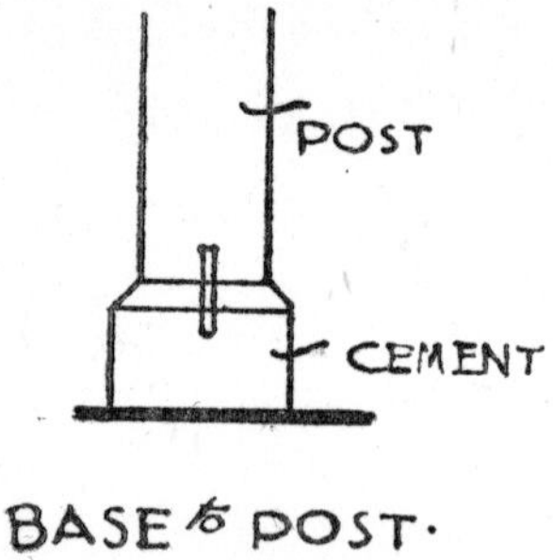

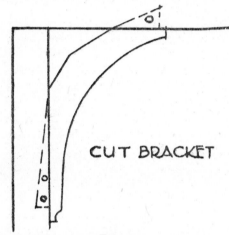

POST

CEMENT

BASE to POST.

FIG. 217.

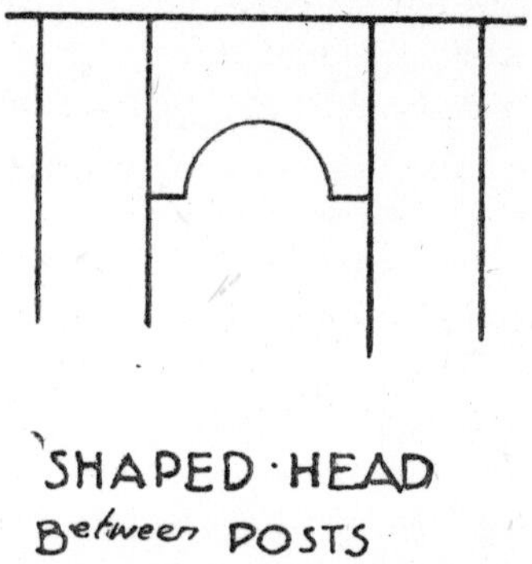

when solid, resting on a lead pad, or a better method still is to erect a small base of brick or concrete to take the foot of the post, having its top edges benched or sloped outwards. The foot of square posts should have a c.i. dowel let into the wood up-

SHAPED · HEAD
Between POSTS
FIG. 218.

wards and into the concrete or masonry downwards. At the head the posts may be either nailed to the beams supporting the rafters, or the beam may be halved over the posts or mortised thereto.

ANGLE BRACKETS.—As stiffeners to the posts and beams over angle brackets are inserted. These are of designs varying from 1″ boarding cut to shapes desired as shown in Fig. 218 to shaped knees or brackets cut out of the solid timber of the same size as the posts and beams as shown in Fig. 219. The latter is an effective form, but at the same time a very expensive one, owing to the large dimensions of timber required for cutting. A splayed tenon should be left on the upper and lower faces, as shown by the dotted line, to fit into mortises cut in the posts and beams, the mortise and tenon being pegged with hard-wood pegs which, in order to give a rustic appearance, are left to project $\frac{1}{2}$″ from the surface. The shaped arches or brackets shown in Figs. 218 and 219 may be either flush jointed or housed into posts and beam.

CUT BRACKET

FIG. 219.

Alternatively and generally in conjunction with panelled posts, cut and carved consoles, or brackets, are introduced in the angles between posts and beams, as shown in

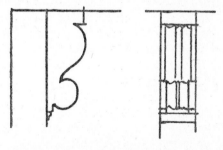

CARVED BRACKET

FIG. 220.

Fig. 220. These should have mortise and tenon joints with both post and beam.

Roofs to Verandahs

As has been said, the roofs to verandahs should, wherever possible, arise out of the constructive require-ments of the building of which they form a part ; but, where this is impossible, they may be roofed with flat roofs where the space is required for use above as a balcony, or the roof may be sloped.

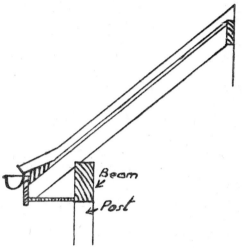

In the last form a beam is run over the heads of the posts as before, and rafters are notched over or bird's-mouthed down on to it run from a wall plate nailed to fixing blocks or bricks in the face of the main wall. Where the rafters are notched over the beam and their ends extended outwards from the beam their feet should be cut splayed, having the bottom splay

FIG. 221.—NOTCHED RAFTERS.

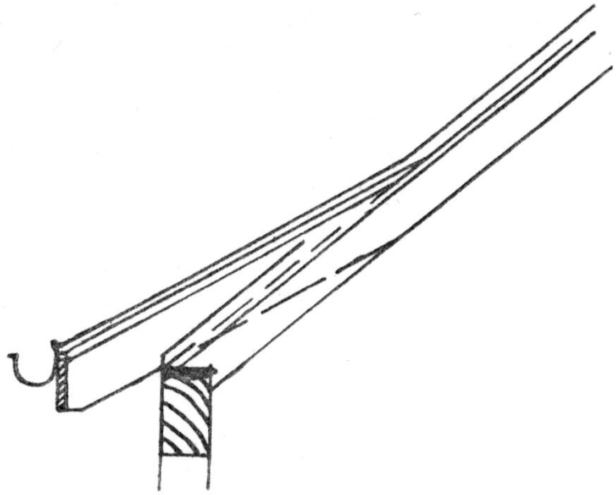

parallel with the horizontal and the upper splay vertical. To this vertical face will be nailed a gutter board or fascia, to which the rain-water gutter will be attached. Where a boxed-in cornice is desired a soffit should be fixed to the bottom, or horizontal splay, on which mouldings may be planted to give a panel effect, being worked in lengths so that the styles will come opposite to the upright posts and as often intermedi-ately as desired.

An alternative method of finishing the feet of the rafter is to bird's-mouth them down on to the top inner corner of the beam and to nail to their upper surface a *sprocket piece*, to the bottom end of which the gutter board and soffit

FIG. 222.—BIRD'S-MOUTH AND SPROCKET.

may be affixed as before described. This method has the additional advantage of altering the pitch of the roof without a tilting fillet being necessary under the tiles or slates. This alteration of pitch is desirable on any sloping surface exposed to the weather when the rain-water is collected into a horizontal gutter, as it has the effect of slowing down the flow at the point of collection, viz. the gutter.

FLAT ROOFS to verandahs, where desired, to be used as balconies, should have the rafters let into the main wall at one end and resting upon the beams at the other. And, wherever possible, labour will be saved by running the floor joists of the bedrooms through the wall and over the verandah. But as, in order to give a good appearance to the outside of the building, the beam will probably have been erected at the height of the tops of the window frames, these, in order that clearance may be allowed over their heads inside the rooms between window, architrave and ceiling, will be some distance below the floor joists. Consequently, studs will have to be framed up from the beam to carry a lighter plate on which the feet of the rafters may rest. The ends of the rafters and soffit may be boarded and treated with a panelled surface or formed into a cornice as desired.

The upper surface of the flat may be either boarded and covered with zinc or lead, or tarred and gravelled, or finished with asbestos cement or other roofing such as Paroid roofing felt. But if it is desired to use the space above as a balcony the addition of movable floors, as already described, will be necessary.

BALCONIES

As previously explained, a balcony is an external gallery which may come over the top of a verandah or be supported on cantilever brackets having a space underneath. Such constructions were popular in houses of the Victorian period, giving access to the outside from windows of upper rooms, and the practice no doubt arose from that of having the drawing-room upstairs ; but with the disuse of that custom the erection of this type of balcony has disappeared from practice ; and, as they were mainly built of metal, they do not enter into the present work.

There is, however, a form of external balcony of which a good deal remains to be said, and which might with very considerable advantage be more frequently introduced into the designs of to-day. The type referred to is that known in America by the incorrect title of the *Sleeping Porch*.

THE AMERICAN SLEEPING PORCH

This is really not a porch at all, but an upstairs verandah, more properly termed a covered balcony. In plan it should be placed so as to give easy access through French windows to a main bedroom, and it should be so formed that at least one, but better two, of its sides are open to the outer air. If it can be conveniently arranged, which will of course depend upon the planning of the rooms, the sleeping balcony should come above the verandah. However, an alternative method is to arrange it in the slope of the roof, in the manner shown in Fig. 224, where an opening is framed as if for a dormer window, but the actual framing of the window itself is omitted.

Whilst the essential feature of the sleeping balcony is that it should be open to the outer air as much as possible, yet a sheltered corner protected from the weather should be provided for the bed. The openings to the outside air should be as large as possible, and permit the breezes to blow across the balcony uninterrupted. To this end nothing of a solid structure is required other than will form corner posts or piers to carry the roofing, or arches to support the ceiling joists. A handrail, either open or closed, at the height of the bedroom window-sills, is all that will be required between the posts or piers, and in it, if solid, should be provided openings at the floor level to allow

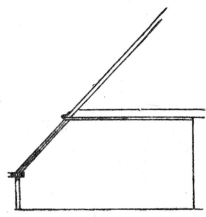

FIG. 223.—SLEEPING PORCH —SECTION.

passage for the rain-water which may collect within. Where additional comfort is desired, and in rainy or exposed positions, the opening may be provided with sliding or folding glazed screens, which may be closed, if desired, on very bad nights.

The floor should be treated as if it were an external flooring, being double and having the upper floor in narrow widths of either teak or oak caulked with tow and red lead, and have the surface painted with white-lead paint. Inside the outer edges of the floor there should also be a sinking run round to act as a gutter and to weep out through the openings already mentioned. The floor should be sloped slightly outwards to this gutter.

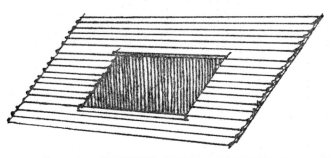

FIG. 224.—SLEEPING PORCH—ELEVATION.

GLAZED SCREENS TO VERANDAHS

For the purpose of additional shelter and for use in winter as a sun-room, glazed screens which can be folded back or removed in summer are sometimes fitted to verandahs. They are in the nature of French windows, being glazed down to the floor line, leaving only a depth requisite for the bottom rail. Where the windows are divided into small panes

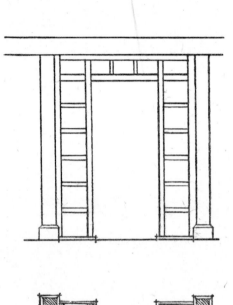

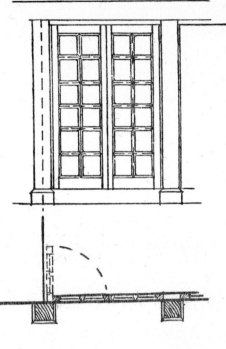

FOLDING GLAZED SCREEN

FIG. 225.

FIG. 226.

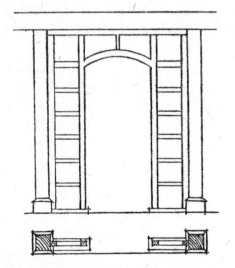

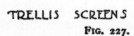

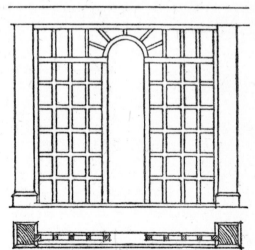

TRELLIS SCREENS

FIG. 227.

FIG. 228.

VERANDAH SCREENS.

182

with bars, the screens should have panes of the same size in order that the scale may be preserved as shown in Fig. 225. If it is preferred to fix them so that they may be folded back against a side wall, as at *c* in the plan, Fig. 226, the two French windows must be hinged at *a* so that the portion *b* may be folded back on to *d* and the pair then again folded back against the wall *c*, where they can be fastened with a clip or turn buckle.

TRELLIS WORK

In place of glass or brackets, verandahs are sometimes filled in partially with wood trellis work to various designs, which are of themselves not unsightly and serve as a useful ground for tying up climbing roses or

FIG. 229.—A SINGLE GATE.

other creepers. In plan the method of fixing is shown in Fig. 227. Where a sill is laid either on the floor of the verandah or at the height of a handrail, as already described, the handrail becomes the sill. Into this sill the sides of a framework of ground are tenoned, being nailed to the verandah posts and tenoned to a head which runs across the opening between the posts and nailed to the beam. Over this framework is fixed the trellis work to design to suit the type of building as indicated in Figs. 227 and 228.

GATES AND GARDEN FURNITURE

CARRIAGE ENTRANCE GATES.—A simple form of single entrance gate is shown in Fig. 229, having a width between the posts of 10' 6", and a height at the heel-post of 4′ 9″. The posts are 9″ by 9″, and the rails and uprights of the gate are 3″ thick. The gate consists, as shown, of four uprights with 1½″ battens spaced 1″ apart in between, having 1½″ braces at their back finishing flush in the angle formed by the bottom rail and the upright, and let into a splayed chase in the angle formed by the middle rail and each upright. There are three rails, top, middle and bottom, which are tenoned through the outside uprights and wedged from outside, being also pinned with hardwood pins through the tenons, or bolted with screw bolts and nuts. All the rails are chamfered on the top edge, and the open part above the middle rail and in between the uprights is fitted with shaped brackets or shoulders housed into a groove cut in the side of the upright and pinned with two hardwood pins in each upright. An oak stump and ball catch should also be provided for fixing the gate to when open.

DOUBLE ENTRANCE GATES.—A double gate made in two separate portions is shown in Fig. 230, having a width between the posts of 10′ 0″. The posts are 9″ by 9″ square, finished with a shaped cap or finial, and each gate consists of a middle rail of 2½″ thick, with a bottom rail 1½″ thick, having battens matched and V-jointed nailed to its outer face and let into the underside of the middle rail. The lower portion of each gate is also braced in the manner described for ledged and braced doors. The upper portion of each gate has a shaped top rail and an open space below filled in with 1″ square uprights set diagonally housed into the top rail and butting on to the middle rail. The uprights are sometimes let into the middle rail, but the practice is a mistaken one, as the weather, gaining entrance, soon causes them to shrink and become loose, whereas if they are nailed at the bottom any shrinkage there may be must find play at the top, where the joint is not so exposed to the weather and consequently less likely to shrink.

Double entrance gates have the advantage that they are not so cumbersome when it is desired to admit a foot passenger as are single gates ; but they have the consequent disadvantage that more work is entailed in giving passage to a wheeled vehicle.

COMPOSITE GATES.—To overcome the difficulty last named, composite gates are designed having either a single carriage gate or double carriage gate, in conjunction with a single wicket gate, 3′ 6″ in width, to one side. Where such are employed it is important that there should be three gate posts so that the carriage gates and the wicket may each work between two posts. Whereas the plan of having only two posts by which the carriage gate, when closed, latches to the wicket gate is not to be recommended.

An excellent double entrance gate and wicket is illustrated in Fig. 231, where the width between the posts is 9′ 0″ for the carriage gates and 3′ 6″ for the wicket. The height at the heel post is 6′ 6″, and the posts 9″ by 9″ or 10″ by 8″, according to design. The rails and uprights are 3″ thick, the lower portions being battened with 1½″ uprights and 1″ cross

FIG. 230.—A DOUBLE GATE.

FIG. 231.—COMPOSITE GATE WITH THREE POSTS.

185

battens at the back. The upper portions are shown here, having an open-work pattern framed out of 2″ stuff cut to a pattern.

All entrance gates may be made of deal, but they will be found more serviceable and not very much more expensive if formed of oak, in which case it is well to bear in mind that any metal work applied should be galvanised or oxidised, as oak rusts unprotected metal which causes unsightly stains on the woodwork.

GARDEN WALL DOORS

An ornamental design for a door in a garden wall is shown in Fig. 232, where the door is formed as for internal doors, but of 3″ thickness and

FIG. 232.—GARDEN WALL DOOR.

7′ 0″ high by 3′ 0″ in width. The upper panel of the door is open, fitted with upright slats or turned balusters let into the rail top, which is shaped to a curve, and the side panels are fitted with frames filled in similarly.

Solid doors are also used, when they are framed together as for entrance doors, having battens vertically placed on both sides and sometimes studded with square-headed bolts.

LYCH-GATES

Though the original purpose of lych-gates has passed into disuse, the form is still used as an entrance to a churchyard. This purpose, it is interesting to note in passing, was a resting-place for the coffin whilst awaiting the arrival of the parson for the burial service, and the seats with which the interior of the gate was fitted were for the accommodation of the mourners. To this fact is attributable the depth of the gateway and the consequent pitched roof, often gabled and hipped with such delightful artistry.

Fig. 233 shows a modern lych-gate which, whilst not conforming to this original purpose, yet has an artistic appearance and is of sound

FIG. 233.—LYCH-GATE.

construction. The height to the ridge is 13′ 0″, and to the eaves 8′ 0″. The total width and depth are severally 13′ 0″ and 10′ 2″, and the width of the gates 6′ 0″. The whole is framed in oak and the roof covered in cleft shingles. The roof is constructed similarly to a hipped roof, but with lighter timbers, the rafters being 3″ by 2″ notched over 6″ by 4″ beams supported by the 8″ by 6″ angle posts from which cut brackets give the necessary projection at the eaves. Cut braces acting as stiffeners to the structure are introduced as shown, and the whole is mortised and tenoned and pinned with oak pins. An 8″ by 6″ base plate supports the sides run along over a 14″ base in brickwork splayed at the top in cement to give the necessary weathering.

A lych-gate of a more fanciful and lighter style, more suitable for an entrance to a garden from a park, is shown in Fig. 234. The height here is 13′ 6″ to the ridge, and the width over all 10′ 0″, the gates being double and 4′ 0″ wide over both.

FIG. 234.—PARK LYCH-GATE.

WICKET-GATES

Gates for side or tradesmen's entrances consist of single gates. The width is 3′ 6″ and the gates are hung between 6″ by 6″ posts and have a height varying from 4′ 0″ to 5′ 6″. They are of $2\frac{1}{4}$″ thick stuff, framed as described for larger gates and, similarly, are preferable in oak.

OUTSIDE GALLERIES.— A form of balcony not much used in modern work, but still to be seen in the yards of inns dating from coaching days, is that of an outside gallery which ran round two or three of the sides of the inn yard. On to this opened doors from the rooms on the upper floor and access was gained to it from the yard by means of an outside staircase. The gallery, and sometimes, as at the George Inn, Huntingdon, the stairs, was roofed by means of the slope of the main roof being carried down and carried on a beam supported by posts having posts or piers under from the ground level. These posts have cut brackets to serve as stiffeners between them and the beam over which, in the arch-way giving entrance to the yard, become the arch head. Above the beam rafters projected from the wall carry the gallery floor, and the posts are carried up square. In between the posts a moulded handrail is run, being housed into the posts. A moulded gutter in wood forms the top member of a cornice at the level of the balcony floor, and turned balusters support the handrail. The stairs are furnished with similar handrails and balusters.

CHAPTER VII

WOOD CARVING

BY GUY CADOGAN ROTHERY

The Call for Craftsmanship—Application of Wood Carving—Tools and Equipment—
Knives—Chisels—Firmer Chisels—Spade Tools—Gouges—Parting Tools—Fluters—Routers—
Punches—Rifflers—Mallets—Saws—Screws, Vices and Cramps—Benches—Machines—Care
of Tools—Woods—Methods—Incised Work—Flat Carving—Chip Carving—Modelled Carving—
Modelling in the Round—Pierced Work—Inlaying—Planted Work—Sunk and Raised Panels—
Hints on the Use of Tools—Design—Period Styles.

THE CALL FOR CRAFTSMANSHIP

HANDICRAFT, although partly eclipsed by machine production, has by
no means been killed. Indeed, of late years there has been a remarkable
and persistent demand for hand work by skilled craftsmen in the building
industry. The demand has, in fact, exceeded the supply, as the difficulty
has been, and still is, to find a sufficient number of efficiently trained men
with an artistic sense. This lack of competent workers is particularly
felt in wood carving. Architects interested in other than very important
buildings complain that it is far from easy to procure the desired men to
carry out good work, bearing the mark of originality in detail and
execution, in moderate-sized houses and the smaller public edifices.
Both the profession and the public appreciate the beauty of fine, appropriate wood carving, and would have more of it were it more easily
come by.

THE RENAISSANCE OF WOOD CARVING

Much excellent recent work in this kind is to be seen in London—
at the Metropolitan Water Board Offices and the Offices of the Port
of London Authority, to mention only two outstanding examples—
and in the provinces. A fair and a growing amount is also to be seen in
private dwellings, while very creditable efforts at restoration have been
carried out in St. Paul's Cathedral and elsewhere.

All this shows that it is fully worth while for woodworkers possessing
artistic talent to take up the study of carving seriously. But for success
something more than skill in handling tools and an appreciation of wood,
with its possibilities and limitations, is needed. There is always room
for the mere copyist, but only to a limited extent. His work, useful
as it is in some directions, does not advance the art or his fortune to any
marked degree. If carving is to do more than maintain the position

it has once again achieved on the decorative side of architecture, and the craftsman is to reap his reward, it is necessary to show originality, either in the design of a pattern or detail, or the free execution of the design supplied. Absolute accuracy in geometric and conventionalised ornament is a mechanical affair and can be accomplished by machines; but that is apt to lead to dullness and decay. It is the craftsman's duty and opportunity to do better, to put life into his work, give it an original aspect, and so make it individual and of enduring interest. This means that the imagination must be trained as well as the eye and the hand.

The Application of Wood Carving

It is improbable that wood carving will again assume the importance in the internal and external embellishment and fitting of a house that it had, say, in the sixteenth century. But with the return of interest in wainscoting for every type of building, and the architectural treatment of fittings, the opportunities for introducing carving are sufficiently extensive. A study of the plates in this book will show this at once.

In ecclesiastical work we find ornamental wainscoting frequently associated with concrete construction, and this note is occasionally repeated in the carving of the main timbers of the roof, the wall plates and corbels. Carving is also introduced on the stalls, benches, screens (for organ lofts, porches, etc.), altar rails and furniture.

In civil and domestic architecture we see wood carving introduced, not only in the ornamental mouldings of wainscoting, but the decoration of panels, cornices (sometimes with elaborate friezes), rails, pilasters and columns. The carving of modern chimney-pieces vies with the magnificence and delicacy of Tudor and Renaissance work. The same attention and care is being bestowed on staircases, with their well-moulded handrails, elaborately turned balusters and newels, or carved splats and panels, carved strings and galleried landings. Permanent screens have been reintroduced in halls and other apartments, and we see carving on doors and doorways, window frames and other internal fittings. In exterior work we find carving applied to porches and entrance door hoods, even to gable ends, balcony woodwork and the lych type of gateway.

However or wherever applied, the carving should be appropriate to its purpose and situation, as well as to the woods used, considerations to be discussed later when we come to problems of design.

Tools and Equipment

Wood carving is among the earliest of the decorative arts, and is to be found among the most primitive as well as the most highly cultivated races, and much of the boldest and the most delicate work has been, and is, carried out with very simple instruments, such as the knife and chisel.

But in the evolution of the art of wood carving an appropriate equipment and range of tools have been designed, and there can be no doubt that the possession of these immensely facilitates the task of the carver. Even the man who is usually content with a knife, a mallet and two or three tools of a general utility type will from time to time, as his work varies, be glad of a full array of tools, many of which are designed for peculiar and perhaps rarely encountered operations. It will also be found that the weight and relative length and stiffness of the tools used should be adapted to the nature of the wood operated upon.

Steel tools should be of the best tempered steel, mounted in solid, comfortable handles. They must be kept in perfect condition, not only well ground, but well sharpened and set. The sharpening and setting of tools are two of the most troublesome operations to the inexperienced carver ; they must, however, be thoroughly mastered.

KNIVES.—Wood carvers' knives usually have short, stiff blades. They are of manifold shapes. The ordinary knife has a round wooden handle with fixed blade of the pen-knife type, having a thick back, a long cutting edge and point. This is for general work of the wittling and slicing order, and is held nearly vertical when in use. Another kind has a curved, short, lancet blade, sharpened both on the outer and inner curve and brought to a sharp point. This is used for paring and simple under-cutting. For most of the delicate work we have several sizes and shapes of short, curved blades fixed at right angles to the handles, as they are used after a drag or scythe fashion. A fourth type has a short, stiff, flat end, sharpened like that of a skew chisel, and is used for roughing out and primitive operations, as in chip carving. It commonly does its work by means of hand pressure, but it will stand the application of a mallet. Knives are rarely used, except on comparatively small pieces and at the bench.

CHISELS.—The carver's chisel is a wedge, being ground and sharpened on both sides. The cutting ends should be rectangular, not rounded. A variety of these have the cutting end bent downward from the rectangular section of the blade, thus acting as a straight-edged scoop. Some have the cutting end bent to right or left, with the cutting edge ground skew-wise, at an angle from the axis of the blade. They are to be had in $\frac{1}{32}''$ up to $\frac{3}{4}''$, then in $\frac{1}{8}''$ to 2". They are general utility tools and used with the mallet.

FIRMER CHISELS.—Strong-bladed firmers are made with cuttings from $\frac{1}{32}''$ to $1\frac{1}{2}''$ wide, either with straight or skewed cutting edge, the latter being known as corner firmers. They are used chiefly for roughing out and grounding out.

SPADE CARVING TOOLS.—These are chisels having the appearance of long-shanked screwdrivers, having a flattened and expanded cutting end widely extended in the fish-tail pattern. They have flat or bent (scoop form) blades, with straight or skew cutting ends. The dog-leg chisel is a spade tool with a double bend downward and a cutting end ground to 45 degrees. The long pod spade chisel has the blade ground well along the shank. They are used for finishing delicate details and also for lining.

GOUGES.—Gouges are most important tools and vary greatly. They are long-bladed chisels more or less curved in section. They usually range to twelve patterns, gradually curving from the almost flat to the complete semicircle or semi-oval, and are made in sizes stepping from $\frac{1}{32}''$ to $1\frac{1}{2}''$ wide. They have both sides of the end sharpened and are scooped well up to the handle. Both straight and curved gouges are made. Bent gouges have short scoops, in the front type bent upwards at the cutting end, and in the back bent with a downward sweep. They are for gouging out the wood, forming mouldings and hollows and similar work. The quick gouge is rather like the letter U in section.

PARTING TOOLS.—Parting tools or dividers are gouges V-shaped in section, different patterns having the sides at more or less acute angles. They are made in sizes from $\frac{1}{2}''$ to $1''$ wide, with both straight and curved blades, and are used for cutting out lines. A spade parting tool is made for very fine work.

FLUTERS, ETC.—There are several valuable modifications of the gouges and dividers. Among these are the fluters, or fluteronis, both straight and curved, with cutting ends having a flat base and sloping sides. The macaroni tool has a flat base and straight sides. They are useful for making mouldings and hollows of these particular sections. The veiner is a small-gauge gouge.

ROUTERS.—Carvers' routers are much the same as the plane known as " old woman's tooth." They have rectangular hardwood bodies or stocks, with a single chisel iron, narrow, fitted in at desired angle by means of a wedge. They are intended for smoothing out wide spaces scooped out by the gouges.

PUNCHES.—These are small rods of steel, circular or square in section, with the ends cut so as to represent a series of dots (arranged in squares, circles, diamonds, triangles, etc.), stars, crosses, rosettes, circles, etc. They are used for punching patterns in flat spaces (much like diapering) and in flutings.

RIFFLERS.—These are all-steel tools with a rasp at one end and a file at the other, which may be straight or curved and having different sections.

MALLETS.—Carvers' mallets should be of moderate size, made of polished beech, with rounded top and sloping sides.

SAWS.—As carving often involves pierced work, compass, pad and fret saws are needed, as well as boring instruments.

SCREWS, VICES AND CRAMPS.—Much of the smaller work is carried out by gluing the piece of wood to be carved to a board, and this board is held in place by means of a carvers' screw, fitted with wing nut, stop and block pad, which is passed through a hole in the bench into the board. Vices and cramps are also required for dealing with larger and more awkward pieces in the workshop, and it is also well to have fret-cutting tables with wood cramp attached.

BENCHES.—Benches should be strong but quite simple, with a hole for screw and good edges for fixing the vices and fret-cutting tables.

MACHINES

A certain amount of " carving " or wood decoration is carried out by machinery, and for motives of economy this is sometimes combined with hand work. For instance, moulding and grooving is frequently done by machinery.

Moulding machines usually have one-piece metal frames, tables which may be provided with dovetail grooves, and are fitted with single or multiple spindles carrying loose heads, to which the cutter block, with appropriate cutter irons, are attached. Such machines, driven by hand or power, will turn out any kind of moulding very rapidly and neatly.

In a carver's workshop, a turning lathe for balusters, small pillar rods and the like, and a fret-cutting machine will be needed. It is unnecessary to give details here, as such machines are fully described in the first volume. They are, of course, merely auxiliaries for preparatory work.

CARE OF TOOLS

It has already been said that the greatest care must be taken to keep the tools in good condition. Wood carving combines the art of the sculptor and the modeller, requiring the greatest delicacy, and a blunt tool, or one with a ragged edge, may do irreparable damage or entail much tedious and unnecessary labour to repair faulty cuts.

A good grindstone is required, supplemented by a Washita oilstone for large, and Arkansas or Turkey oilstones for smaller, tools. Special bevelled gouge slips, tapered stones, and others shaped for parting tools, macaroni, etc., are procurable.

For the final setting of knives, chisels and gouges, leather strops, to be covered with emery paste, are needed.

Chisels of the firmer type should be ground to an angle of 25 degrees and sharpened to an angle of 35 degrees. Other chisels have a finer cutting edge.

A common error in grinding and sharpening parting tools and others of this type is to wear away the upper sides so that a point or projecting cutting edge is produced at the base. This not only weakens the tool, but makes it more difficult to work, as the wood is rather pressed forward than cleanly cut. It is better that the base should be, if anything, slightly behind the upper edges.

The cutting edge should be perfectly straight and smooth, and to keep this fine setting repeated stropping is desirable.

WOODS

In Chapter VI of Volume I it was pointed out that the woods generally chosen for carving purposes are oak, lime, pear, holly and box. Many others, however, are available, and, indeed, very few woods have not been used at one time or another, or in small pieces, for carving.

The great point is that the wood should be free from knots, shakes, fissures, wany edges and, to a reasonable extent, of resin. But it is fair to say that pitch-pine makes a capital carver's material. A number of recently introduced Colonial woods have done excellently in the carvers' hands, notably jarrah, teak, Burma mahogany, Indian silver-grey wood and Koko-wood.

It may be observed that while the silver grain of oak and the rich colouring of walnut enhance the beauty of carving, too distinctive figure or sharp contrasts of colour are inimical to pleasing effects, by distracting attention, producing undesired illusions of light and shade, and sometimes even introducing a grotesque note.

Of the oaks, the English and Austrian are the best. American is too coarse, and wainscot oak too hard and highly figured.

American walnut is rather hard, therefore requires heavy tools. English walnut is softer, but has close, even grain ; it is best dealt with by light, sharp tools. It is pleasing when coloured but not too figured. Italian walnut does well.

Mahogany, if carefully chosen, answers admirably. Cuba, West Indian and Burma are the best. Short tools are advisable.

Teak carves well and is very suitable for outdoor work. So are the pines, especially pitch-pine.

Jarrah is hard and somewhat coarse, but it cuts well if too thin tools are not used.

Box, pear, sandal and satin woods are adapted for delicate work, especially finely sculptured figure and portrait detail, much of which was formerly " planted " in solid furniture and wainscoting. Satin wood is rather uncertain ; rose wood and ebony effective but difficult.

Lime and holly are soft, of even colour and grain, very suitable for elaborate detail. Lime and holly carving was often " planted " and applied.

In selecting wood for carving, it is always wise to have regard to its texture and the character of the design. Large, boldly and freely carved work can be carried out in coarse or open-grained woods, such as oak, chestnut, mahogany, walnut and lime ; but for fine, intricate work even, close-grained wood, such as pear, apple, box and ebony, are best.

Carvers will find it easier to work across the grain than with it, and this will influence the choice of tools at the different stages of operation.

METHODS

Wood carvers should endeavour to cultivate boldness and freedom, both in design and execution. And to this end it is advisable for them to commence on large work, using chiefly the knife and chisel. Delicate work can come later, when a sense of freedom has been acquired. Carvers are rather apt to look at their work from the bench level, with the result that they fiddle with detail, much of which is lost when the finished piece is placed in position. But unless the final position of the work is taken into consideration, the desired effect cannot be assured. This can be better appreciated with large work, not too highly finished; for if such a piece is placed above eye-level, it will be quickly realised that special treatment of detail is desirable for such " skying," the upper parts being emphasised so as to produce a certain amount of oversailing, which will produce the illusion of balanced evenness. If this is not done, and equal emphasis given to all parts, the base will assume greater prominence, and the upper part will be obscured. The reverse is the case if the carving is placed below the eye-level. In other words, the carving must be looked upon as part and parcel of the architectural whole. When this attitude is adopted, the suitableness of each kind of treatment, and of particular cuts to a given design, and the position it is to occupy, will be more clearly understood. Special care has to be taken when dealing with staircases, balconies and galleries, as then there is frequently a conflict of vision.

For small and moderate-sized work, especially of the panel description, the wood to be carved is glued to a backing of common plank, not less than 1″ thick. This is done by placing spots of hot glue on both pieces of wood and pressing together until dry. The wood is then made secure to the bench by means of the wing-nut bench screw. It is then ready to be operated upon. Ungluing is done by gently pressing a chisel all round between the two boards and prising apart.

Larger pieces are held in position by vices or cramps, or bench hold-fasts. Occasionally work has to be carried out on the wood in position, very often in connection with repairs. This will render benches, trestles or some other kind of scaffolding necessary, and calls for a very sure eye and hand on the part of the craftsman.

The design or pattern is drawn freehand, directly on the wood. Or the drawing is traced and transferred to the wood by the help of carbon paper and tracing over the lines. When this is done, the next step is " lining in," that is to say, cutting a line round the edge of the design with a parting tool. This preserves the edge. If the carving is to be in high relief, " wasting away " is the next process, which is cutting away with the firmer, appropriate gouge or router, the surrounding ground, which is to remain flat. By wasting away, greater freedom is obtained for the use of tools on the actual carving. The second operation of actual carving is " setting in," which is to cut round the edge of the design with tools suited to the curves, to define the outline. For high relief this operation is repeated with greater force, and is called " bosting " or " boasting." Then comes " grounding out," removing the superfluous wood as in " wasting away." Finally comes the finishing, which may involve chiselling, gouging, the use of the knife, fluters and punches. All will depend on whether the work is to be in low, medium or high relief ; flat, modelled, undercut or in the round ; and the kind of cuts used.

INCISED WORK.—Incised work is the most primitive form of carving. In this type the design is carried out more by incised lines, direct cuts, dots and circles. The lines may be plain cuts made with the knife or of a more pronounced kind carried out with the parting tool, or one of the fluters, so producing a cut with sloping edges or a groove with a decided section. There may be a combination of such lines, while the dots, circles and similar ornaments may be punched or cut with the chisel. Flat parts of ornament and grounds may be punched to produce diaper patterns, or scored with parallel, cross-hatched or spiral lines.

FLAT CARVING.—In this type there is little or no modelling of the pattern. The design is lined in with the knife or parting tool and the superfluous wood wasted away. The result is that the pattern stands out from the background, but has a flat surface. If the knife is used, the sides may be quite straight ; if the parting tool is run in the orthodox way, the sides of the design will be chamfered. The degree of chamfer will depend upon the kind of parting tool used and the angle at which it is held. It is obvious that for this kind of work to be effective, the design must be bold, free from niggling details. It is well adapted to the Celtic spirals and interlacing bands and Tudor strapwork. Backgrounds, and even broad expanses of the pattern, may be punched with repeat ornament.

CHIP CARVING.—Although the term chip carving was only introduced in 1888, the thing itself is very old, coming immediately after plain incised work. It is a type of carving which can be carried out with an ordinary straight-bladed knife, or a knife and chisel, and the characteristic cut is the diamond with chamfered sides, forming a low pyramid. It is what is sometimes called " notching," and may be most conveniently carried out with the parting tool, which will give the required chamfer and V-shaped channels. Gouges and chisels can be used for wasting away. It is specially adapted to geometric designs. But the characteristic cuts and ornaments are often found in association with more elaborate carving, being introduced in bands and so on.

MODELLED CARVING.—Modelled carving calls for the highest skill and gives the greatest variety in both form and light and shade. In this, after lining in and bosting, the design is finished with appropriate tools to give all the parts a rounded, modelled form, with raised parts and sunk parts, in which gouges of all kinds, the veiner for delicate channelling, and fluters are required. Modelled carving may be in low, medium or high relief. The higher the relief the more modelling is required. But it is to be observed that high relief carving is most liable to distortion whenever placed out of the direct line of vision. In elaborate work, this tendency should be corrected in the execution, and this is where skilled craftsmanship shows to advantage, which by modifying an artist's drawing, does so only to stick the closer to its spirit and give it the more faithful rendering.

" Undercutting " is much associated with high relief carving. It is carrying out the modelling so as to nearly detach the ornament from the background, a style largely resorted to by the later Renaissance workers and very noticeable with the work of Grinling Gibbon and his school. Indeed, the Gibbon school often undercut to such an extent that portions of ornament are actually cut away from the background, being attached only at one or two points. It is introducing us to modelling in the round.

MODELLING IN THE ROUND.—Modelling in the round is wood sculpture. It includes figure work, foliated finials and cresting, though this last generally falls into the next type. The craftsman in this tries to conform to nature as closely as possible ; but some conventionalising is necessary. All the tools described are used in this work. The wood is first roughed out to the desired shape at the carpenter's bench, after which the sculptor sets to work in earnest, slowly whittling and paring away until the actual form and detail gradually appear. The amount of finish bestowed on the work will depend upon its size, the conception of the artist and the position the completed piece is to occupy. But the scope for the carver is practically unlimited, and may even include surface decoration, for instance, on the drapery of figures. This surface decoration can be carried out with the knife and chisel or with punches.

PIERCED WORK.—A good deal of architectural carving, especially of the modelled order, is pierced in parts. This is often introduced in Gothic geometrical and floral tracery ; in Saracenic geometrical work ; to a lesser degree in Renaissance scrolling and conventional or realistic floral designs. In the case of small piercings the operation is begun with a gimlet or other boring instrument, and carried on with the knife and gouge. The pad saw is used for large piercings, to be finished with gouges. Rifflers are also handy in putting finishing touches to small, narrow piercings. In some instances cresting and pierced panels, fret-saws and benches are used for the preliminary stages.

Pierced work of the Oriental type very often is not carved work in the ordinary sense. The panels are built up with short rods and prismatic cubes, turned in the lathe separately, or carved, and then put together, sometimes with sections of fret-cutting, by gluing or, in better-class work, by secret pegging or nailing, with an occasional tenon. The secret pegging and nailing is carried out by drilling holes with fine gimlets through two pieces and driving in the nail (usually headless wire nails or thin brads), gluing the pegs in such a way that the fastening is covered up. The tenons would be used only for the heavier pieces, generally those fitting close against the enclosing frame. For screens and staircases, screens made up of fancifully cut prisms, or scrolled tracery (fretwork) with a central oval or circular carved boss, look very well.

INLAYING.—Wainscoting, screens, etc., ornamented with carving, may be further adorned with inlay, usually as banding, borders, corner pieces or central panels. The usual practice is to sink a band or panel by scoring the outline with a stiff knife, or the parting tool so held that the outer side of the tool is placed vertically. The cut is made barely $\frac{1}{32}''$ deeper than the width of the veneer to be used. From the cut the wood is wasted away to an equal depth, using bent gouges for the purpose; finishing with a fairly smooth surface. The pattern is then drawn on the veneer and cut out with a veneer knife, which has a short, stiff blade with skew cutting end. For delicate work a lancet form of knife is used. The pieces are then fitted into the sunk channel or panel and eased where necessary. It is always wise to cut to full measure and then ease by careful paring, as the veneer should make a tight fit, but not so tight as to induce splitting or buckling. If a simple pattern of the chequer order is being used, the work is fairly easy. It is when the parts have curved and complicated outlines that difficulties arise. If we have completely sunk channels or panels, it will be necessary to cut a counterpart to the design in a contrasting coloured veneer. Then this counterpart, with the pattern left blank, is first fitted in, and when fixed in position the pattern is adjusted and fixed. For fixing, hot glue is spread thinly over the sunken parts and the veneers pressed in firmly, and a weight placed over them until dry. When thoroughly dry, it may be necessary to finish with glass or emery paper, to secure a perfectly level, smooth surface. Natural coloured woods, such as holly and ebony, are much used for this purpose, but a greater variety of woods can be used, and even stained veneers, to obtain greens, blues and various tints. Glass paper should be sparingly used on stained woods.

PLANTED WORK.—Much of the carved decorative work of the Renaissance, such as drops, swags and delicate festoons, the pateræ and lighter ornament of a later period, were carved in small pieces, often in the round, in lime, pear or holly, and then applied to wainscoting or door frames of other woods. This may be done by concealed nailing and pegging, or simply by gluing, but sometimes the carving is done on a shallow base, which is fitted into a corresponding groove or sunk panel scooped out of the wainscoting, door panel, frame or what-not. This process is known as planting. It implies better work and permanency than gluing or even concealed pegging and nailing, but it is not very suitable for large or heavy pieces; these had better be framed, as explained in the next paragraph.

SUNK AND RAISED PANELS.—In the best class of work, sunk and raised panels are carved in the solid, but this is expensive. The usual practice is to carve the panel as a separate piece and then frame up. In this way the effect of cavo-relievo carving (raised carving in sunken channels) can be secured easily. Here there is direct co-operation between carving and joinery.

HINTS ON THE USE OF TOOLS

Wood offering a fair amount of resistance, and in most cases only short cuts being used, it is necessary to have a firm grasp of the tools. These, except when wasting away and bosting on large work, should be held nearly vertical, though this does not apply to the fluters or, as a general rule, to the gouges. The parting tool, while essentially an instrument for cutting V-shaped grooves or their reverses (Λ-mouldings or raised lines), can make other effective cuts. Thus one side can be held in a true vertical line, which will give a straight side and at the same time help to waste away superfluous wood ; or it can be used for chamfering. When this tool is held in a nearly vertical position we have the slide cut, useful in paring down edges ; when held at an angle and pushed forward steadily, we have the sweep cut, for lining-in and making curves. But the carver, anxious to secure bold, artistic effects, will have to pay particular attention to the knife and chisel and the nice use of the mallet. When hard wood is being dealt with and long cuts made, sharp taps are delivered with the upper part of the mallet ; in closer modelling, the lower end of the mallet serves better ; and in very delicate work, hand pressure on the chisel will be sufficient. The skew chisel is very handy for removing wood out of corners and also in undercutting. The spoon-shaped or entering chisel serves for levelling grounds in confined spaces. The spoon-shaped or entering gouge is reserved principally for hollowing out undulations in foliage, and with this for work on leaves, flowers and fruit, the veiner, macaroni and other fluters are used, together with the double bent gouge, which is also helpful in all kinds of hollow work.

DESIGN

In the majority of cases where wood carving is required for the decoration of buildings, the carver is supplied with detailed drawings which he has to copy as faithfully as possible. Sometimes, however, he has only rough sketches to go by ; and more rarely he may have only hints to guide him, or he may be given a free hand. Nevertheless, the carver will always have the chance of impressing his individuality on the execution, the treatment of detail, in which he may happily be allowed a certain amount of latitude. Therefore, it is necessary for him to possess some knowledge of the principles of design and acquire facility in drawing. Design is largely a matter of good balance and fitting ornament to use and situation. Balance does not necessarily imply strict symmetry. Even in geometric patterns we need not have exact repeat ornaments to secure symmetrical balance. If the mass value of the corresponding parts are equal, there may be considerable difference in the ornaments. When we come to conventional designs with flowing lines and curves, or more realistic treatment, the differences may be still greater. We may obtain equally satisfactory balance if we take a panel and place four approximately similar corner pieces in the angles and a central ornament which if divided by a line down the middle would give two exact halves ; or if we place a patera, or similar ornament, in the left lower corner and have a curved spray the upper two-thirds on the right and meandering towards the centre. In figure pieces we may have one figure towering in the middle, with others, smaller, seated, kneeling, tailing off on both sides, so as to form a triangle, such as would fill a pediment or tympanum ; or we may have a more natural grouping, provided the figures are so arranged as to form a pleasing composition, which will be at once pictorial and decorative and without confusion or violent distraction (one of the signs of bad design), carrying the eye to centre or right and left.

Appropriateness also plays a great part in good design. Size and total mass must be suited to the expanse of wood to be decorated and to its surroundings. A very large, bold design tends to dwarf dimensions and will often look absurd in a small space—a little, low-pitched room. On the other hand, a small design, full of fine detail, is apt to be lost if placed high or in a large, lofty apartment. Mention has already been made of the need to give emphasis to the upper or lower part of a carving, according to whether it is to be placed above or below the natural level of vision. This is partly a matter of execution, but should also be taken into consideration in designing, as it should influence the disposition of masses.

Another aspect of appropriateness as regards wood carving is a matter of the general design of the woodwork, and that is that the carving should not be placed where it would be incommodious. Thus, in a staircase with elaborate carved newels, balusters or panels and strings, the handrail should be smooth. On stalls and benches we may have arms, side wings, legs and stretchers carved in high relief, but the backs and seats should be smooth or ornamented with incised or very simple chip carving. In wainscoting carved ornament had better not be below the line of vision, unless it be on pedestals on consoles.

Wood carvers should have, in addition to their carving tools, pencil, compasses, dividers, set-squares of 45 degrees and 60 degrees, and semi-circular protractors. But instruments should be used with discretion in preparing design. Even in geometrical patterns there is a danger of losing feeling by striking lines by means of instruments. That veteran craftsman, L. F. Day, points out two of these dangers. He says: " The first is the inevitable hardness which results from geometrically struck lines, and the second is the constraint it imposes upon the invention of the artist." So he advocates the drawing of the design freehand, then setting out mathematically with vertical and horizontal lines the obvious geometric divisions, adding whatever radiating lines are necessary, and then filling up firmly and freely without help of instruments. The lines are merely the skeleton on which the artist adds the flesh, and it gives the whole design life.

This leads us to points concerning the carver directly. " Planes of relief, light and shade, and texture," says Walter Crane, " being the chief means of expression in carving, much depends upon the feeling and taste with which these resources are utilised so as to give appropriate contrasts of surface, while the entire design should be in keeping with the construction and use of the object it is intended to adorn." For this purpose a close study of natural objects is desirable and the cultivation of a free, flowing touch with the pencil. "The lines and spiral curves of wood shavings, or curls of thin paper," Crane goes on, "which have been rolled, are useful to study for fresh suggestions in the treatment of scroll forms so useful in carving, and for the treatment of heraldic mantling and lambrequin. Heraldic forms are, indeed, pre-eminently adapted for treatment in wood carving, and a study of heraldry in its finest periods is strongly recommended to wood carvers." As we see by quite recent work, heraldry is far from losing appreciation among admirers of carving. Animal and human figures, as handled by feudal heraldists, have sound lessons to teach, for they impart a sense of "the rhythmic arrangement of the main lines and limbs in action, and also the controlling influence of an unseen boundary, within which your animal or figure should be designed—square, parallelogram, circle or oval, which last will probably be the most useful. In the treatment of figures in wood carving, drapery is always a very important element, as being one of the chief means of giving richness and colour to a design. Well-designed drapery also helps to express movement of life in figures, besides giving broad planes or rich fields to contrast with the smooth and delicate modelling of the faces and finer details of the hair, costume and accessories."

It should be observed that detail must always be subordinated to general outline, otherwise good design will not be attained or will be obscured.

A wood carver anxious to make headway as a designer and a craftsman should make a study of old examples and set about acquiring a knowledge of styles and the characteristic treatment at different periods. For it should be obvious that to be successful the wood carving must harmonise with its surroundings, and that can only be obtained by avoiding the clashing of styles in design and treatment. Formal chip carving which would look well in Tudor surroundings, or the rude modelling which would be appropriate in a cottage and simple interior, would look out of place amid rich or delicate decoration. And it will be seen that this applies quite as much to execution as to design.

PERIOD STYLES

In a short sketch such as this it is only necessary to deal with period styles as they influenced woodwork in the British Isles.

Probably the earliest examples of woodwork came from the Saxon times, and the carving in these unmistakably shows the influence of Celtic culture. It is mostly incised line and dot work ; involved spirals being intermixed with elongated scrolls, very slightly foliated, often merging into grotesque animal forms, with groups of dots and circles.

Some of this ornament was carried on into the Norman period, which is that of the chip-carving technique, with its simple forms of geometric patterns, the raised and sunken diamonds and triangles, the chevrons or zigzag lines, dentils, bird's head and beak, with a few grotesques, including cats' heads, human masks and very elaborate mouldings, often containing nail-head, billet, cable, stars and other ornament. Geometric and interlacing chip carving was at its best during the thirteenth and fourteenth centuries. Foliage and flowers were also introduced, in a highly conventionalised style.

Gothic work is remarkable for the use of foliage and flowers, growing in complication and naturalistic leanings as the centuries went by. The trefoil is characteristic of Early English, the ball flower of the Decorated period, with the quatrefoil and the introduction of tracery both in flower and geometric forms. With the Perpendicular came the vine, wild and Tudor roses, oak leaves and apples, pine-cones, parsley leaves, with many other flowers and leaves treated at once naturalistically and decoratively. Gothic work is notable for its elaborately carved finials (usually in the shape of unfolding buds), cusps and crestings. Heraldry was also conspicuous, complete shields, with helms, crests and mantlings, being used, as well as crests, badges and isolated heraldic devices, which included a wonderful menagerie of reputed beasts of the field and birds of the air with fabulous creatures. The linen fold, which came in with the fifteenth century, small and rather formal, became very liberal and beautiful, with voluptuous lines in the sixteenth, and disappeared before the advent of Henry VIII.

The early work emerged from chip carving to refined modelling, and towards the Tudor period we find the coming of the strapwork, which was in part an elaboration of the Celtic spiralling, though on a broader and less involved pattern. Strapwork, narrow, flat bands, is often combined with mild scrolling, heraldic ornament and figure work. At this period Renaissance ornament, chiefly architectural, in the form of Classic pilasters, columns and entablatures also came in, being more or less harmonised with Gothic decoration. Under Elizabeth the rather grotesque swellings on columns and pilasters occur, often covered with arabesque or strapwork carving in low relief. This was continued into the Jacobean period, when we also find the jewelling (an elaborated form of the chip class of ornament), consisting of diamonds, fusils, circular and oval bosses and portrait medallions. The termini figures emerging from diminishing pilasters, and serving as caryatides or not, introduced towards the end of the Tudor period, became more common. With Charles I and Charles II we are more frankly in the Classic period. Inigo Jones introduced a somewhat heavy style, greatly enriched by Sir Christopher Wren, under whose auspices Grinling Gibbons and a flourishing school of wood carvers were kept busily at work. They were somewhat exuberant but wonderful craftsmen, treating flowers, leaves, fruit, birds and game naturalistically, and making much use of amorini, cherubs and heraldry. Most of this was in high relief, practically in the round. Ribbon and drapery treatment and the sculpture of the human form were remarkably good. This was essentially the age of drops and festoons, often adorning doorways and window openings. Early Georgian work is marked by the heavy Classic style of William Kent, associated with the closed and broken pediment, with elaborate Classic mouldings and scrolling, including expansive and contorted acanthus leaves and termini figures. The carving was rather bold, nearly coarse, much of it being in pinewood and gilded. In the mid-Georgian period, under Sir William Chambers and Thomas Chippendale, wood carving was lighter, but more contorted, being influenced by the French rococo and the Chinese styles, in which we see fantastic, lop-sided scrolling, reeds, waterfalls, pagodas, shells and rocks, with amorini, queer birds and floating ribbons. Under the influence of the Adam brothers, wood carving became more sober, either rather heavy Classic architectural forms, in a bold relief, or the low relief ornament of the Herculaneum period, with its classically draped figures, sphinxes, tripods, fans, paterae, honeysuckle patterns, slight acanthus leaves and the delightful fuchsia drop. After that there was a falling off as regards quantity and quality of wood carving until the revival in the present century.

Finally, it may be pointed out that Gothic work should be carried out in oak, and towards the Decorated period with the addition of chestnut. These woods are also most appropriate for Jacobean work. Walnut, lime, pine and cedar are most suited for Renaissance design, and mahogany for Neo-Classic work; with pear, apple, box, holly and ebony for finer work.

While the rarer coloured and figured woods (rosewood, Kingswood, etc.), and the richer coloured Colonial woods, would give the sense of anachronism if used for distinctly Gothic ornament, they would not be so inappropriate for Renaissance and especially Classic motifs. Gothic woodworkers used the common native woods, obtaining colour by in-laying or painting the wood. But in Classic architecture there was a greater variety of timber, with richer natural colouring, and this har-monises with the style.

INDEX